Dedicated to
The Betterment of
Agriculture in America
As Stated in
The Creed of the Future Farmers of America:

"I believe in the future of farming, with a faith born not of words but of deeds — achievements won by the present and past generations of agriculturists; in the promise of better days through better ways, even as the better things we now enjoy have come to us from the struggles of former years."

# North Putnam FFA Chapter

Roachdale, Indiana ● Chartered 1952

1975-76 Officers: President - Mike Blackmore; Vice President - Jesse Ader; Secretary - Tony Wheeler; Treasurer - Dean Williamson; Reporter - David Lane; Sentinel - Ernie O'Hair. Members: Max Blackmore, Rick Douglas, Kevin Kendall, Duane Kiger, Dallas Lane, David Lawless, Jeff Lawson, Mike Lytle, Mark McFarland, Mike Miller, Rick Pressley, Jim Robertson, Bryan Sheets, Doug Southwood, Jeff Stultz, Eric Uhls, David Wallace, Terry Wood, Bruce Fowler, Tim Poynter, Jeff Davies, Max Zaring, Brian Clark, Gary Fitzsimmons, Roger Early, Dennis Higgins, Roger Gibson, John McGuire, Dennis Deaton, Denny Sutherlin, Laren Livesay, Doug O'Hair, Mark Cook, Tim Lawless, Mitch Nichols, Kevin Bray, Rick Stultz. Advisor: Steven E. Cash.

# PREFACE

As George Washington once stated to Congress: "I know of no pursuit in which more real and important services can be rendered to any country than by improving its agriculture."

American agriculture — which grew from a country of small farms to a nation of large mechanized units in 200 years as told in this volume — depended on people for progress. Likewise, the future evolvement of agriculture, both farming and agribusiness, demands the leadership of the American people.

The future belongs to the youth, and so it is in agriculture, too. Young people, such as members of the Future Farmers of America whose primary aim is to develop agricultural leadership, cooperation and citizenship, offer hope for the further extension of United States agriculture.

It is with this hope for the future that we present the accomplishments of agriculture in this book as a commemoration of America's Bicentennial.

Officers of the Indiana State FFA Association, chartered in 1929, are, left to right: Treasurer — Jerry Ott; Vice President — Kent Crosby; President — David Parker; Secretary — David Bechman; Vice President — David Sheets; Reporter — Mary Ann Lutes; Vice President — Tim Webb; Sentinel — Rick Crum. [1975-1976]

# THE GROWING OF AMERICA
## 200 YEARS OF U.S. AGRICULTURE

John Rupnow

Carol Ward Knox

Published by
Johnson Hill Press, Inc.
Fort Atkinson, Wisconsin


Distributed by
Nasco
Fort Atkinson, Wisconsin

**The Growing of America . . . 200 Years of U.S. Agriculture**

Library of Congress Catalog Card Number: 75-24680

Original concept suggested by A.E. Haller, Vice President, Director of Research and Development, Nasco; Consulting editors — Donley V. Henning, William D. Ardell, Ronald A. Miller and Dean C. Bork; Book design — Thomas W. Jewell; Production Supervisor — Reuben J. Corrigan; Cover design and photo — Richard G. McIntyre.

# TABLE OF CONTENTS

# From Small Acorns and Little Fishes

One of Sir Walter Raleigh's men gave this account of what he saw on Roanoke Island off the coast of Virginia in 1584:

"The Indians sent us diverse kinds of fruits, melons, walnuts, cucumbers, gourdes, peas, roots and fruit very excellent; and of their corn which is very white faire and well tasted and groweth three times in five months; only they cast the corn into the ground, breaking a little soft turf with a wooden pickax . . ."

Indians rescued the starving colonists and taught them how to plant and cultivate the New World crops. It's doubtful the colonists could have survived the rigors of their new environment without help from the Indians.

In fact, the fundamental system of Indian cultivation remained essentially the same for much of our agricultural history. The Indians planted corn first. They selected the best ears and dropped four to six kernels per hill, the hills four feet apart. Indians near water also put a fish in each hill, along with the seed. As the fish decomposed, it released plant nutrients. Squash, beans and pumpkins were planted between corn hills.

Indian-domesticated plants taken over by the colonists are said to provide 57 percent of the value of total farm production today.

Two hundred years ago, nine out of every ten working persons were on a farm. And the average farmer used some of the same farming tools and practices that were used in Biblical times. The colonial farmer, like the Indian, was mainly concerned with merely surviving.

Today, each farmer in the United States grows food and fiber for himself and 53 other people.

The amazing course of agriculture over the 200 years traced in this book is a tribute to the resourcefulness and ingenuity of the American farmer.

**Indians rescued the starving colonists and taught them how to plant and cultivate the New World crops.**

*Facing page:* Indians raised corn, pumpkins and tobacco in this scene from the Indian village of Secota. Space was left between the rows "so one stalk would not choke the growth of another". Watchmen were posted in the fields to scare off birds and other pests. A large feast was prepared in the village street for the celebration which followed the dance to the gods of agriculture. The only known portrayals of Indian life from the 16th century were painted by John White and Jacques Le Moyne. Theodore de Bry bought these paintings and used them in publishing *Hariot's Book On Virginia* (1590).

# English Land Grants 1606-1732

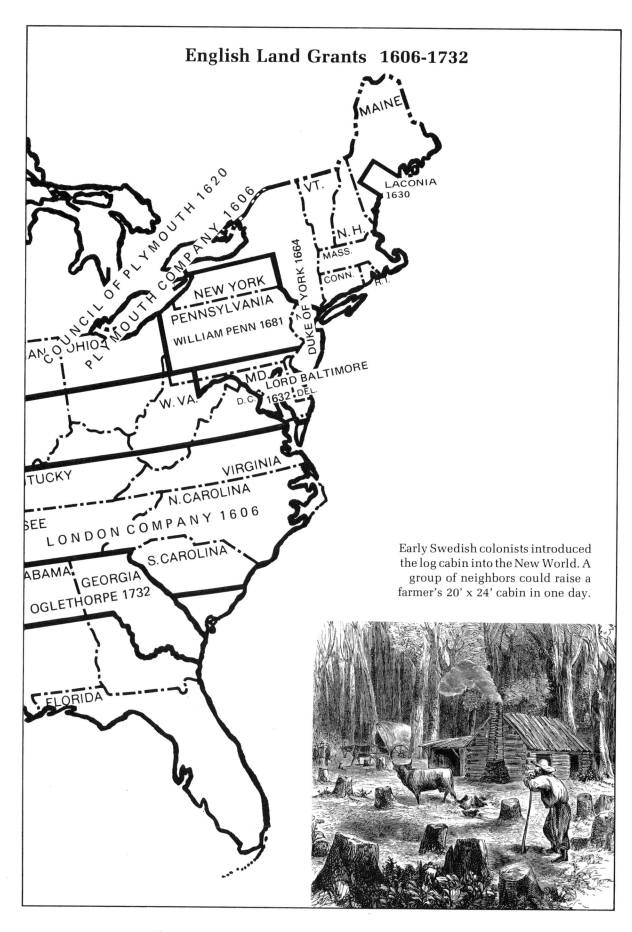

MAINE

LACONIA 1630

VT.

N.H.

MASS.

CONN.

R.I.

COUNCIL OF PLYMOUTH 1620

PLYMOUTH COMPANY 1606

AN OHIO

CO.

NEW YORK

PENNSYLVANIA

WILLIAM PENN 1681

DUKE OF YORK 1664

MD.

LORD BALTIMORE

D.C. 1632 DEL.

W. VA.

TUCKY

VIRGINIA

N. CAROLINA

SEE

LONDON COMPANY 1606

S. CAROLINA

ABAMA

GEORGIA

OGLETHORPE 1732

FLORIDA

Early Swedish colonists introduced the log cabin into the New World. A group of neighbors could raise a farmer's 20' x 24' cabin in one day.

The King granted large sections of land to proprietors and trading companies, who distributed it to new settlers through the Colonial government. This set the stage for American land policy in the 19th century.

# I
# At Liberty to Break New Ground

## 1775-1800

The old bellman was waiting in the steeple. A little boy ran out of Independence Hall shouting, "Ring! Ring!" Somebody else shouted, "It has passed!"

It was July 4th, 1776. The Declaration of Independence had just been adopted.

The Continental Congress resolved that printed copies of the document be distributed. On July 8th, they were ready.

Philadelphia began to celebrate at noon. That bell, with "Proclaim liberty throughout all the land unto all the inhabitants thereof" carved on its curve, led the ringing.

By nightfall Trenton, New Jersey, was celebrating. Everywhere — in the Continental Army and at the crossroads — the Declaration was publicly presented. George Washington had it read to the troops at six o'clock on the night of the 9th. It had been over a year since the minutemen/farmers had been fired upon at Lexington and Concord. Who knew what lay ahead?

The War for Independence brought people together — farmers, particularly, because almost everyone was a farmer in 1776. The war gave farmers a more general knowledge of what was going on around them.

As communication became a little easier and more frequent, farmers heard about new farming methods and new lands for settlement. The shock of the Revolution alone was enough incentive for many to pack up and move to the interior. At that time the so-called inexhaustible West was central and western New York and the eastern Appalachian area.

Moving was easy. A good, strong farmer could carry all of his equipment — except the cart — on his shoulders.

By 1775 some specialization in farming had started to develop. Keeping some livestock became popular, especially in the older eastern settlements. Some farmers in Rhode Island kept upwards of 100 cows. On one farm 73 cows produced 10,000 pounds of butter in five months, or an average of nearly a pound per cow per day — an exceptional yield. Ac-

When the Revolution began many farmers became minutemen. At a minute's notice they would drop reins and plow handle to respond to the cause of liberty. They introduced a new concept into warfare.

More than half the signers of the Declaration of Independence were farmers. Danger was something these men learned to live with. Button Gwinnett, after signing the Declaration and returning home to Georgia, found his farmstead burned to the ground. He was forced into hiding in the Georgia swamp. Other farmer/signers also suffered the same fate.

cording to the census of 1850, the average number of pounds of butter produced per cow per year was 51 in Rhode Island and 91 in New York. (The production of one of today's better cows would yield about two pounds of butter per day.)

Improving livestock became important to some early farmers. Robert Bakewell started selective improvement in England in 1760, crossing various breeds and sizes of longhorn cattle. Later, Collins experimented with shorthorns, Tomkin and Price with Herefords, and the Duke of Bedford with Devons. Back in Baltimore, H.D. Goff, Ringold and Mathew Patton sent to England for improved stock in 1783. Two years later, one of the bulls received was sent to Kentucky.

Justin Morgan was foaled in Massachusetts in 1793, laying the foundation for the fast-trotting Morgan Horse — ideal for use on the better roads pulling hacks and light carriages.

Fine-wooled Merino sheep were brought to the colonies from Spain. Du Pont de Nemours (of gunpowder fame and founder of the chemical company) bred them and sent several to New England and Ohio.

The first improved hogs were produced from a pair of pigs sent from the Duke of Bedford to George Washington. The courier who was assigned to guard the pigs on the trip across the Atlantic promptly sold them when he arrived in this country, so Washington never did benefit from the gift. But many other farmers did.

The Woburn or Bedford hogs, as they were known, came from a Chinese/English cross. A 1792 description recalled, "They are splendid animals, with many fine points, mostly white, somewhat spotted, small bones, deep round barrel, short legs, feeding easily and maturing early, often weighing at a year or a year and a half old from 400 to 700 pounds with light offal and the first quality of flesh." The Byfield hog bred in the United States came from a Chinese/common hog cross and became popular in Kentucky, Ohio and the West.

In the late 18th century each colonial farm was a self-sustaining unit, growing food for home needs and a little surplus to be traded for sugar and salt. Tools and clothing were homemade. Crop rotation meant grain/grass/fallow.

Cotton moved into the South, first to South Carolina and Georgia, then westward. Cotton had been grown in colonial times, but mostly for domestic use. The first cotton spinning patent was registered in 1738. Several refinements, and the development of Watt's steam engine in 1769, revolutionized the weaving of cotton cloth.

The southern climate provided good growing conditions for the green-seed short-staple cotton. The problem came in separating the seed from the fiber. It was a slow and expensive process.

Sea Island, a longer-staple cotton, was easier to separate

The Morgan horse was developed in 1793 with the foaling of Justin Morgan in West Springfield, Massachusetts. The Morgan breed was a genetic mixture of Thoroughbred and Arabian.

The Spanish Merinos were first introduced to the United States in 1793. The large amount of oil in their wool was said to counteract the tendency of native wools to be dry and brittle.

Before improved breeds were introduced to the new country, hogs were scrawny. They were forced to scrounge for a living because farmers thought that allowing their livestock to run at large would toughen them. Improved breeds were introduced from England in the 1790s to upgrade the colonial stock.

Eli Whitney made cotton king in the South with his invention of the cotton gin.

from the seed, but it did not produce well in areas away from the coast. So, short-staple cotton was grudgingly accepted.

In 1791 the U.S. exported 138,000 pounds of raw cotton. Exports jumped from 1.6 million pounds in 1794 to 6 million pounds in 1795. The reason for the sudden increase: Eli Whitney's cotton gin. Whitney's invention made separating the seed from the fiber practical, and upland or short-staple cotton became the largest commercial crop in the South. Cotton built a base for the southern economy.

Rice and sugar production advanced rapidly during the post-Revolutionary period. Sugarcane was introduced into Louisiana in 1751, and Etienne de Bore proved during the 1790s that it could be grown successfully. In 1794 a revolution in Santo Domingo drove out French sugar plantation owners who settled in Louisiana. They introduced Creole cane from the French Caribbean Islands.

George Washington and Thomas Jefferson were among the leading agricultural reformers in the late 18th century. They experimented with crop rotation, new fertilizer, new crops and improved livestock.

Washington's farming abilities are not generally appreciated as much as his military and statesmanship accomplishments are. But there was no doubt he was a farmer and a good one. The *Cultivator* of 1800 gives us some clues about Washington's love of the land:

"The farm of General Washington at Mount Vernon contained 10,000 acres of land in one body — equal to about 15 square miles. It was divided into farms of convenient size, at the distance of two, three, four and five miles from his mansion house. These farms he visited every day in pleasant weather, and was constantly engaged in making experiments for the improvement of agriculture.

"Finding that the cultivation of tobacco exhausted his land, he gradually substituted grass and wheat as better suited to the soil. He began a new method of rotation of crops, drawing up an exact scheme by which all his fields were numbered and the crops assigned for several years in advance.

"Some idea of the extent of his farming operations may be formed from the following facts: In 1787, he had 500 acres of grass; sowed 600 bushels of oats, 700 acres of wheat, as much more in corn, barley, potatoes, beans, peas, etc., and 50 with turnips.

"His stock consisted of 140 horses, 112 cows, 235 working oxen, heifers and steers, and 500 sheep. He constantly employed 250 hands, and kept 24 plows going during the whole year when the earth and the state of the weather would permit.

"In 1786 he slaughtered 150 hogs for the use of his family and provisions for his Negroes, for whose comfort he had great regard."

Washington was always experimenting. In 1788 he hired a German gardener and started work on several seeds and plants. First, it was East India hemp. Then Jefferson sent him a bag of pecans, some French evergreens and herbs. Then he tried tree cotton. Five thousand white thorn came from England. He also worked with varieties of turnips, some chicory (for coffee), Botany Bay grass (to control erosion), cloves, new varieties of apples and even seeds for a cucumber tree.

The King of Spain sent Washington two jacks in 1788. Lafayette sent him a jack and two Spanish horses and Washington bred some fine mules.

When the British Agricultural Society was founded by his friend, Sir John Sinclair, Washington was made an honorary member.

At the age of 29. George Washington was already a prominent Virginia farmer.

Tobacco was an important cash crop in the South. Hogsheads (63- to 140-gallon barrels) of tobacco were shipped to England, and were one of the country's first major exports.

Mount Vernon covered thousands of acres. George Washington enjoyed directing the operations of his farm, and conducting agricultural experiments.

On July 20, 1794, President Washington sent a letter to Sir John: "It will be some time, I fear, before an agricultural society with congressional aid will be established in this country. We must walk, as other countries have, before we can run; smaller societies must prepare the way for greater; but with the light before us, I hope we shall not be so slow in maturation as older nations have been."

Some early colonial farmers long felt a need to organize — to at least set up societies devoted exclusively to agriculture. The American Philosophical Society founded in 1743 and the American Academy of Arts and Sciences founded in 1780 had encouraged the investigation of European agricultural experiments. The Philadelphia Society for the Improvement of Agriculture and the South Carolina Agricultural Society were founded in 1785. These groups were the first to publish their findings and results.

The Massachusetts Society for Promoting Agriculture, incorporated in 1792, published a series of papers known as the *Agricultural Repository*, the best of its kind in its day.

It was a long time before the academic reports were spread around, but these societies were pioneers in the great task of agricultural education.

The Revolutionary War brought a quickening of the national consciousness. An American trumpet called for the creation of a new country with a distinctive way of life rather than a borrowed one from the Old World. Practical farmers began to look for new crops, new methods of farming and new lands.

The original states with western claims gave them to the Congress of the Confederation. The Continental Congress resolved on October 10, 1780, "that the unappropriated lands that may be ceded or relinquished to the United States by any particular state . . . shall be disposed of for the common benefit of the United States and be settled and formed into distinct republican states which shall become members of the federal union and have the same rights of sovereignty, freedom and independence as the other states . . ."

The Peace Treaty of 1783 recognized American independence and gave the United States control of a vast domain south of the Great Lakes and west of the Alleghenies.

Thomas Jefferson was appointed to a committee to draft a plan for eventually surveying and settling the western lands — the Ordinance of 1785. This ordinance provided for surveying the western lands into townships of 36 sections of one square mile or 640 acres. Section 16 of every township was to be reserved for the maintenance of public schools. Lands could be sold to the public for cash at not less than a dollar per acre. This ordinance also fixed straight and exact boundaries for the new lands.

The Ordinance of 1787, considered by some historians to be the most important piece of legislation passed by the Continental Congress, set the mode of disposing of lands in the western territory. It was generally followed with reference to all territories from the Appalachians to the Pacific.

New states were to be admitted on equal terms with the

On the 3rd of November, 1783, the final treaty of peace between England and the United States was signed in Paris. Benjamin Franklin, John Jay and John Adams represented the United States. When John Adams was presented to King George III as the first minister of the United States to England he said: "I must avow to your majesty, I have no attachment but to my own country." "An honest man will have no other," was the King's instant reply. This cartoon portrays the final settlement.

**The New Nation 1783**

original 13 states. The West was bound to the nation by equal rights. Slavery was prohibited, and specific guidelines were set forth as to territorial and state boundaries and admission.

These ordinances were a vital force in determining the westward movement of settlement and agriculture.

The federal land policies which developed created two different schools of thought: One group urged prudence in disposing of public land, the other advocated a generous land policy. These divergent views affected the course of the history of American land policy.

As the settlers moved from the Atlantic coastal plain to the interior, new areas were opened for development and new tillage methods were required. The plows they used, for example, varied almost as much as the number of blacksmiths who made them, and often proved to be less than satisfactory. One commentator gave his objections: "It broke and crumbled the furrows and was difficult to hold; easily thrown out of the ground. Cultivating to any depth was difficult without the help of one or two men riding on the beam to help hold it down. It did fair work on light and easy soil, but the share and the moldboard were so attached as to make the wedge too blunt which made the friction excessive."

Changes and modifications were obviously in order. The first patent for a plow in the United States was issued to Charles Newbold of Burlington, New Jersey, in 1797. Made of cast iron, the moldboard, share and landside were all cast together. This created a disadvantage because the whole bottom had to be discarded when one section wore out. The Newbold plow, in spite of its imperfections, was such an improvement that in 1807 John Peacock paid Newbold $500 for the privilege of copying some parts of the cast-iron model.

Men like Thomas Jefferson and Daniel Webster personally studied the implement and made proposals for improving it. Jefferson wrote a treatise in 1798 on the form of the moldboard. He calculated mathematically its exact form and size and especially its curvature with a view to reducing its friction.

The Revolutionary period marked the beginning of a general improvement in farming. Men and societies with new techniques and machines were the forces created by the Revolutionary experience. They planted the seeds for an agricultural revolution peculiarly American.

MAKING READY FOR CULTIVATION.

To prepare the ground for cultivation, trees and shrubs had to be routed out of the ground and destroyed.

Charles Newbold's cast-iron plow patented in 1797.

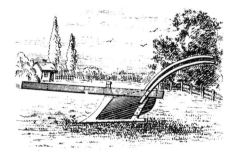

# II
# Meeting the
# Challenge of
# the New Frontier

## 1801-1830

"Bound for the promised land" became a popular phrase in 1800. The treaty of Greenville in 1795 had cleared the way for peaceful settlement in the Old Northwest. The Napoleonic Wars created chaos and hundreds of thousands of Europeans immigrated to America's eastern shores. Many of them then went west with the early settlers trying to escape the economic depression of 1801-1803.

Frontier farmers in favor of liberal land policies applied political pressure in 1800 to change the terms of the land act of 1796. This specified the purchase of 640 acres as a minimum at $2 per acre. A buyer was required to pay one-half the price in cash within 30 days and the remainder within another month. In 1800 the terms were changed to one-fourth cash down, one-fourth in 40 days, one-fourth within two years and one-fourth within four years. By 1832, 40 acres was the minimum; in 1854, $1 per acre was set for land that had been for sale for 10 years and 12½¢ on land that had been listed for 30 years.

Thomas Jefferson's efforts at this time were most significant. He arranged the Louisiana Purchase in 1803 — probably the greatest real estate bargain in the history of the country. Not only did he increase the total area of the country by 140 percent, he bought it for $14.5 million. That was just 3¢ per acre! The lush prairies and rich bottomlands were suddenly opened to the frontiersmen-farmers and they drooled at the opportunity.

Lewis and Clark explored the new territory from 1804 to 1806 and truly opened the doors for a steady migration westward. Land was the attraction.

Land — virtually limitless amounts of virgin soil — was available, according to the newspapers and handbills of the time, simply for the asking. The temptation was irresistible for the farmer sweating over worn-out ground in Virginia. Immigrants, too, were pleased to find that all they had heard

"The future destinies of our country hang on the event of this negotiation," said Thomas Jefferson of the Louisiana Purchase. This acquisition is said to be the greatest achievement of President Jefferson's administration.

The Erie Canal connected the Hudson with the Great Lakes. The canal cost $10 million which was paid off in nine years through tolls.

Digging the Erie Canal was a long, hard task. Teams of horses hooked up to a large stump puller helped rid the area of tree roots.

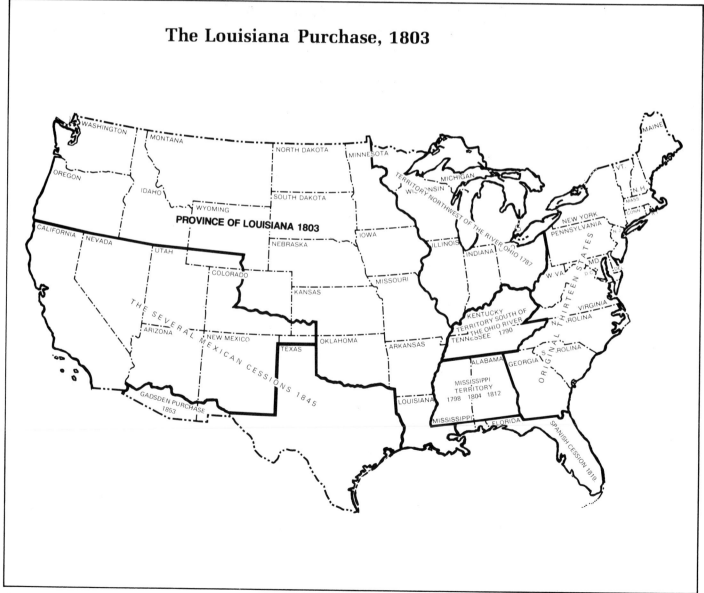

## The Louisiana Purchase, 1803

about the New World and its opportunities was true — at least, that's what they read in the papers. The Louisiana Territory was on its way to becoming a rich agricultural region, and the breadbasket of the world.

The Cumberland Road — running 834 miles from Cumberland, Maryland, to Vandalia, Illinois, was constructed at a cost of $7 million — and provided an overland route to the Mississippi River. Steamboats replaced the man-powered keelboats of the day. By 1830 some 200 steamers were working the inland waterways, carrying home-seekers and goods on the Ohio, Mississippi and Missouri Rivers.

The Erie Canal connected the Hudson and the Great Lakes in 1825 and cut travel time from 20 to 8 days between Buffalo and New York City.

These developments opened the way for quick settlement and, just as important, gave farmers greater accessibility to eastern markets.

Between 1803 and 1820, Ohio, Indiana and Illinois joined the Union. Population in the old Northwest Territory jumped from 272,000 in 1810 to 1.4 million in 1820. And the flow of corn, oats, wheat, bacon and beef to the Eastern Shore was established.

The end of the trail for the Cumberland Road was Vandalia, Illinois, which provided the connecting link with the Mississippi River.

The parade of plows continued — each one different and usually a little better than the one before.

R. B. Chenoworth of Baltimore patented a cast-iron plow in 1808 with share, moldboard and landside in separate pieces, which could be replaced when they wore out or broke. Jethro Wood carried the action a step further with a patent issued in 1814 for a plow with interchangeable parts fastened together with interlocking parts that could be forge-welded together. But Lady Luck frowned on Jethro Wood. He sent one of his plows to Czar Alexander I of Russia who returned the favor by sending Wood a diamond ring. One of Wood's "friends" got the ring and kept it.

Wood spent the rest of his life promoting the cast-iron plow against an army of adversaries, among them patent infringers who he thought were his friends. The Wood family reported he received not more than $500 for his invention.

People fought the cast-iron plow for amazing reasons. It was accused of poisoning the field, causing rapid weed growth and "draining the strength right out of the soil". Twenty-five years of poor crops in some areas were blamed on the cast-iron plow.

The plow wasn't the only tool that came under a lot of criticism. An 1826 report made to a New England agricultural society said, "A plough, a harrow, hoe and shovel, with a small sprinkling of forks and rakes comprise the whole range of most farm tools and these are so ill-constructed requiring in most cases twice the power to use them, uselessly consum-

The covered wagon was the home between homes. It carried all the settlers' earthly belongings and provided the shelter from the elements on the long trip to a new life.

ing time, talent and temper" — to say nothing of the wear and tear on the Puritan conscience.

The grain cradle was generally accepted during this period and saved untold hours at harvest. The cradle was no more than a device attached to the scythe to hold the grain after it was cut. This meant the grain could be laid on the ground in a small pile, making it easier for the farmer to bind it.

Agriculture was the basis of the westward movement that everyone else followed. Nearly all of the pioneers were farmers. Without them there would have been little reason for merchants, manufacturers and others to join the trek.

The flow of settlers continued — down the Wilderness Road, up the Potomac and through Pennsylvania. Fifty-dollar covered wagons plowed over almost impassible roads, carrying a man, his family and all their worldly possessions. When they got to a major river, the trip would continue by water on a flatboat or steamboat, then overland again.

Upon arrival at a selected spot, the farmer built a log cabin or lean-to the first season and proceeded to clear enough land for the first year's crop.

During the second year the neighbors got together for a house-raising. It was a social event and the pioneers found ways to have fun . . . at least their children did.

Whitewash was used to cover the surfaces on the inside of the cabin for a fresh, clean appearance. But at one house-raising in West Tennessee, a group of children had different ideas. While their parents were hard at work, they tiptoed to the woods where the horses were tied. When it came time for the house-raisers to go home, they found all of their horses looked alike . . . white with cropped tails. After a great deal of frustration and confusion, the horses were finally sorted out and the people went home.

There is no report available on what was done to the young whitewashers!

Cooperative efforts, like house-raisings, were both social and practical affairs. For example, a settler might invite his neighbors to a logrolling — if he needed some trees cleared. With horses and oxen the logs and brush were rolled into piles and burned. The ashes were leached and lye was boiled down until a gray potash was left. This was frequently shipped east and sold to soap manufacturers.

When the trees were removed, the early farmers found a rich, black loam — ideal for raising corn, oats and barley. Top yields of the day from some of this ground included 60 bushels of corn per acre, along with 50-bushel oats and 40-bushel barley. Apple, peach and pear trees were common and provided dried fruit for the winter diet.

Wheat was harvested and flailed at the rate of 8 to 16 bushels a day. Some bigger farms had circular threshing floors. Oxen or horses were driven over the grain to thresh out the kernels.

Corn harvest was entirely a hand operation. It was shelled by rubbing the ears over the edge of a shovel. Later it was ground in a mortar — a hollowed-out end of a stump — or in a handmill consisting of two stones which created a grinding action. Some farms had primitive cider and cheese presses. Wild game and berries added variety to the diet.

Many settlers brought a cow or a few pigs and chickens to a new settlement. The farmer kept ownership of his livestock with a brand and allowed them to run in the woods. Milk cows were brought back at night, usually tempted with some salt. At first, no hay was cut for winter feed. Selected slippery elm, white elm or pignut trees were cut down, and the herd was driven into the woods. The cows ate the buds and shoots.

Corn was grown primarily for home consumption. Extra corn was fed to the pigs or occasionally distilled into whiskey. Livestock were driven to a river and flatboated to New Orleans. After the flatboat arrived in town — loaded with livestock, bacon, hams, corn, tobacco and skins — the goods were marketed and the boat broken up and sold as lumber. The settler bought a horse with some of the proceeds and made the trip back overland.

Frontier farm life in the Ohio River Valley was filled with hard work and homey chores. Linsey-woolsey, a linen and wool mixture, was the favorite cloth. It was spun and woven under the porch roof and dyed with hickory or butternut bark.

The daily drudgery and monotony were made bearable by a variety of activities. Sewing circles, quilting bees, husking bees, hog killings, spelling matches, singing schools, school

The sickle and scythe were important reaping tools. Later the grain cradle came into general use. A device was attached to the scythe which held the grain after it was cut.

Keelboats were first used to transport home seekers and goods on the inland waterways. They were later replaced by steamboats.

Backbreaking physical labor was a major part of pioneer life. But the farmer also took time to relax with his family, read the weekly paper and keep posted on what was happening around him.

Like all other crops, corn was cultivated in a primitive manner. Scarecrows were hung to frighten away the birds.

programs, sheepshearings, camp meetings, church meetings, barn-raisings, logrollings, box socials, weddings, country dances and house-raisings were all used as excuses to get together with friends and neighbors. An evening of socializing was not complete without the older boys plugging a chimney, moving a wagon onto a roof or tipping over a privy.

The boys of the family were trained in splitting wood, building fires and churning butter. Young ladies did the milking. The young men poured the melted tallow into the candle molds, chopped the sausage meat and boiled the water for butchering. On stormy days they helped their sisters clean and card the wool, wind the yarn and hetchel (soak and beat) the flax. Later, they might help dye the homespun and bleach the linen. They searched the woods for good trees to make ox yokes, and hickory saplings for splint brooms, and were expected to be able to make chair bottoms and baskets after the splints were cut. They guarded the cornfields from squirrels and crows and set traps for wolves and skunks.

Along with these duties went some pleasures, such as hunting for grapes and wild honey, going nutting and berrying, and assisting in sugaring-off by carrying the buckets of maple sap and water and tending the fires.

All life was not romantic and pastoral on the frontier. People suffered from fevers. Epidemics, childbirth and malnutrition took a large toll. Too few doctors were too far away.

Mosquitoes were unbearable. Large swarms of flies seemed to be everywhere in summer. Many farmers lived a mean and commonplace existence. Their children grew up dirty, malnourished and ignorant with little opportunity for a better life.

The industrious and thrifty pioneer farmer cleared more of his farm each year, built a better house and barn, and increased his holdings. He kept a few cattle and sold his products at the nearest town or to traveling traders.

He was glad to see the value of his farm increase as more land was improved in his area. He had surplus money to buy better implements and improved stock. He could build fences and drain lowland. His children not only finished the country school, but were later sent for higher learning.

Going into Indiana and Illinois, the frontier settlers found open prairie land between the forest belts that lined the rivers.

Prairie agriculture differed from that of the forested regions. Little clearing was necessary, so the farm was brought under cultivation more quickly.

A three-tined-wooden hand fork helped early American farmers with their chores.

After being husked, the corn was shelled by rubbing the ears together or over the edge of a shovel or tub. The corn was then ground in a mortar for feed.

However, the thick and matted prairie soil was a formidable challenge to the customary wooden and cast-iron plows. Sod-busting busted more farmers than sod. From three to seven yoke of oxen were required to break a new field in some areas. After the sod was broken, a crop of corn could be raised the first year by dropping the seed into the break between the furrows or a slit made by an axe. At the end of the season, the sod, if it had not been plowed too deep, may have rotted and the field could be cross-plowed. Sometimes it took two or three seasons for the roots to rot enough to make for easy plowing.

A crop of wheat was sown while the corn stubble was left to keep the protecting cover of snow from being blown off during the winter. The fresh prairie soil was fertile and could yield from 50 to 100 bushels of corn, 25 of wheat and 40 or more bushels of oats or barley.

The government reduced land prices to $1.25 an acre in 1820. Land offices were established at various points and on certain days, advertised beforehand, the land was offered to the highest bidder at auction.

As the day for the land sale approached, scores of anxious prospective buyers gathered, waiting the chance to get choice acreage. From the active buying that followed came the expression "land-office business".

The greatest danger on the prairie was fire. Dry grass covered vast stretches of open land in late summer and fall. Wind-driven fires burned thousands of acres.

As a precaution, it was necessary to surround the house, barn and fields, with belts of plowed areas. Even then, flying sparks would sometimes jump the fire belt and all the labor of years could be lost in minutes. Backfiring or controlled burning of the dry grass around the buildings and fields was another protective measure.

Like the eastern pioneers, the first prairie settlers sometimes became dissatisfied or felt crowded. Then, according to one account, "he decided to move when a good chance comes to sell out to a more prosperous land seeker. The bargain being concluded, he stows his plunder underneath the cover of a large wagon, harnesses his four horses before it, hangs his bucket beneath and his feedbox behind, starts his two cows on in advance, sets his eldest boy on the right-hand wheel horse with a single rein in his hand and commences his journey west, shaking the dust of the Yankee settlement from his feet."

Wheat could be threshed with a flail at the rate of 8 to 16 bushels a day.

Some farms had a threshing floor. Around this track horses were driven over the grain to thresh out the kernels. The straw was then removed and the grain was winnowed.

# III
# Sifting and
# Winnowing

## 1831-1850

Many settlers pushed ahead of the public lands survey into the public domain and took up squatters' rights on choice locations. According to the law, these squatters were violating land policy. In some areas, attempts were made to dislodge the squatters by military force. But the frontier farmer prevailed. In 1841 Congress passed legislation which allowed heads of families, men over 21 and widows to settle on 160 acres of unsurveyed public land with an option to purchase their holdings at the minimum price when the land was placed on sale. The Preemption Act of 1841 was another victory for those who advocated a liberal land policy.

From 1820 to 1850 over 2,000,000 immigrants crossed the Atlantic and Pacific. Over 500,000 Germans alone came to America between 1830 and 1850. People from every country in Europe, China and Africa were part of this migration.

The Texas annexation, acquiring of the Oregon Territory and the California gold rush combined with the railroads to lure the people west.

Eastern agriculture underwent two major changes in the 1840s. In response to the growth of a home market, farmers gradually shifted from self-sufficiency to commercialized agriculture.

While this process was taking place, internal improvements such as canals, railroads and overland roads were making it possible for the frontier farmers to ship their agricultural products to eastern markets. So, eastern farmers were forced to specialize to supply a market in the nearby urban centers and avoid western competition.

The westward movement to the prairies caused a new problem. The cast-iron plow was fine for turning the virgin soil the first year. However, in succeeding years, the soil stuck to the plow and the farmer had to stop every few feet to scrape the plow surface. In the forest regions the soil became more compact and harder to plow as it was tilled year after year.

One member of Congress wrote in 1834 that it was his opinion the prairie land would have to be abandoned for farming because it was too sticky. He concluded, "God hath

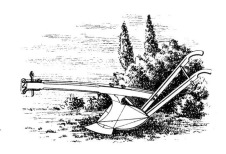

In 1834, Jacobs patented a plow with a coulter attachment for cutting the turf.

**The westward movement to the prairies caused a new problem.**

As the frontier pushed further west, proprietors sold lots to ready pioneers. Hamburg, Illinois is a small village situated halfway between St. Louis and Quincy on the Illinois/Missouri state line.

# 100 LOTS IN THE TOWN
## OF
# HAMBURG

### Will be offered for sale to the highest bidder (on the ground) on
# Monday, August 15th, 1836.

This town *site* is situated on the east bank of the Mississippi river, about forty miles above the mouth of the Illinois river, and is half way between St. Louis and Quincy. It will be observed that this is the only high bank upon the east side of the Mississippi river, for one hundred miles below Quincy, and consequently must be the landing place for an extensive country in *Illinois* and *Missouri*, as a reference to the map will show.

As it is not intended by the Proprietor to puff the said town in handbills and newspapers, it is only necessary to inform the public of the time and place when and where the LOTS will be offered for sale.

If gentlemen wishing to select a situation for business will take the trouble to examine for themselves, they will perceive that an immence trade can be opened on both sides of the Mississippi river, at wholesale and retail. And it is conceded by all persons acquainted with the place, that it will be the interest of

## Mechanics in Particular

To select this place on account of its healthiness as well as the convenience with which they can supply themselves with the best of timber of all kinds. One acre of ground will be given to any individual or company that will erect a STEAM MILL upon it (within such time as shall be agreed upon.) This situation for the carriage without the expense of the *ways* generally used at Saw Mills; also the grain to be received by land on one side and from boats on the other side of the mill. The Flour and Lumber to be shipped without drayage at all stages of the water.

## HAMBURG

Has a larger body of good building timber in the immediate vicinity than any town on the Upper Mississippi or Illinois rivers, and also an inexhaustible quantity of good building and lime stone, which will in all cases be given without price when used at the place. The best of spring water is convenient to all parts of the town, and one very large spring might, at a trifling expense, be conveyed into the fourth story of any house that may be erected.

### *Liberal inducements will be offered to Mechanics to locate in* this *town.*

Due regard has been had to reserving suitable public grounds for such purposes as the religious or political interests of its inhabitants may require—also a spacious market place. The entire length of the town has a good landing which is to be free to all steam and other boats to land at to discharge and receive freight, and also for the purpose of repairing, *free of expense*, forever. A State Road passes through the town and the FERRY crosses the Mississippi river at this point, which is a main leading direction from Boonslick and Salt River settlement and the country generally north of the Missouri river for travelers going east to the States of Illinois, Indiana, &c. and it is believed it will be the great crossing place above the National Road. Good boats and careful hands are always ready to cross travelers and emigrants, also stock of all kinds without a moments delay.

## A STEAM FERRY BOAT

Will be built for this ferry next year, and all persons that come to buy goods at HAMBURG lots will be free to cross both ways, in the boats at their regular trips, gratis. A liberal donation will be made for a good public house, provided it is erected soon.

N. B.—Gentlemen desirous to select a situation upon the bank of the "old father of waters," say about eighty miles above St. Louis, also same distance below Quincy, and sixty above Alton, are particularly referred to Captains and Clerks of Steamboats for a description of Hamburg. It is 20 miles from Carrollton, 30 from Atlas, 30 from Pittsfield, in Illinois, and 15 from Clarksville, 9 from Paynesville, 12 from Auburn, and 18 from Troy, in Missouri.

The sale to be continued from day to day until all the lots are offered.

### ☞ Terms made known on the day of sale. ☜
### JOHN SHAW, Proprietor.

*Hamburg, July 22, 1836.*

The steel plow served the American farmer well. Some farmers were particularly brave, and strung the reins around their necks as they guided their horses and plows down the field.

not ordained that the hellish black earth be seduced." Try and tell that to an Iowa, Illinois or Nebraska farmer today!

The blacksmith in nearly every small town turned his attention to adapting the plow. What was needed was a moldboard so smooth that it would scour.

About 1833, John Lane, who had a small blacksmith shop on Lake Michigan in Chicago, made the first steel moldboard from an old crosscut saw and an iron frame.

A blacksmith at Grand Detour, Illinois, was the most successful. His name was John Deere and he built his steel plow in 1837. Deere took a heavy, circular steel saw and carefully shaped it over a log pattern. This plow turned the sticky soil better than any other available. John Deere and other companies began to manufacture steel plows. Up to the year 1855 there had been no less than 372 patents issued for changes and improvements on the plow.

The early moldboards were designed to operate at the speed of a walking horse. The man who could open a field by plowing a straight line and follow that act with an encore of straight furrows was considered to be an accomplished farmer.

Most farmers strung the reins through the thumb and forefinger of each hand while gripping the wooden plow handles. But other more daring men wrapped the reins around the body fastening them in a knot. Then, with a gentle sway or grunt, the horses were manipulated down the field. If the horses were spooked, the results for farmer and plow were disastrous. Where extra labor was available one person drove the horses and another gripped the handles.

Another back-breaking chore that received considerable attention was grain harvesting. In 1833 Schnebley of Maryland patented a machine for reaping. Obed Hussey's reaper was more extensively and successfully used, but Hussey's poverty kept him from marketing the machine on a large scale.

Cyrus McCormick patented his reaper on June 21, 1834. (Further improvements were made in 1845.) This machine would cut about 12 acres a day. One man drove the horses and another walked by the side of the reaper raking the grain off the platform.

In the summer of 1855, the American machines took on international competition in Paris. Each machine had one acre of oats to cut. Three machines were entered for the first trial — one American, one English, and one from Algiers — all cutting and raking at the same time.

The American reaper cut one acre in 22 minutes, the English, one acre in 66 and the Algerian cut one acre in 72 minutes. At a later trial on the same place three other machines were entered — one from America, one from France and one from England. The American machine again cut an acre in 22 minutes, while the two others broke down.

The winning competitor "did its work in the most exquisite manner," said a French journal, "not leaving a single stalk

McCormick first tested his reaper in 1831. N.C. Wyeth's perception of the event shows McCormick following behind as his trusted helper, Joe Anderson, runs the machine.

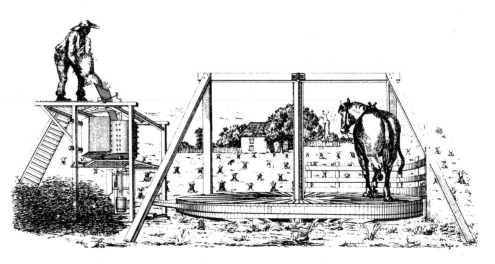

McCormick made various improvements in his reaper. The machine he patented in 1845 included a safety seat for the operator so he wouldn't have to walk.

ungathered, and it discharged the grain in the most perfect shape as if placed by the handful for the binders. It finished its piece most gloriously."

"All the laurels," said the report of a French agricultural journal, "we are free to confess, have been gloriously won by Americans and this achievement cannot be looked upon with indifference as it plainly foreshadows the ultimate destiny of the New World!"

Many attempts were made at inventing a threshing machine. The earliest had a series of flails attached to a revolving cylinder. Later, wooden pegs were set in the cylinder to catch and beat the grain. In 1850 a separator was attached to the thresher for winnowing.

At the trial of threshing machines at the Paris exhibition, Americans won with a machine invented by Hiram A. and John A. Pitts. During the contest six men were engaged in threshing with flails. In one hour they threshed two bushels of wheat. In the same time Pitt's American machine threshed 24 bushels, Clayton's English machine threshed 13 bushels, Duvoir's French machine threshed 8 bushels, and Pinet's French machine threshed one-half bushel.

A French journal reported, "This American machine literally devoured the sheaves of wheat. The eye cannot follow

Horsepower ran this threshing machine that was patented in 1834.

the work which is effected between the entrance of the sheaves and the end of the operation."

Mowing with the scythe or sickle was at best one of the toughest jobs on the farm, notwithstanding the efforts of poets to make people believe otherwise. A farmer used nearly every muscle in his body because of the twisting motion — an unusually great exertion. It is not surprising that mechanical ingenuity was directed to lighten that work load.

The first mowing machine which met with any success was patented in 1831 by William Manning of New Jersey. In 1834 the Ambler patent was granted. This mower was a wrought-iron cutter bar and a single smooth-edged knife operated by a crank making a vibrating motion.

The character of agriculture was changing rapidly. Factory growth and the use of improved farm machines took away from the home and farm much handwork that had been a part of agriculture since Biblical times.

The railway made it possible for agricultural products and machines to be transported longer distances.

NEW ENGLAND FARMER

DEVOTED TO AGRICULTURE AND ALL ITS VARIOUS KINDRED ARTS AND SCIENCES.

Honor waits, o'er all the earth, The art that calls her harvests forth.—Bryant.

VOL. I.          SATURDAY, JUNE 23, 1849.          NO. 14.

S. W. COLE, Editor.          QUINCY HALL, BOSTON.          J. NOURSE, Proprietor.

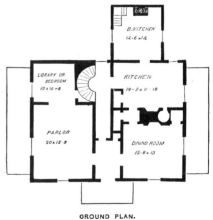

GROUND PLAN.

An increase in agricultural publications and newspapers and the invention of the telegraph also helped improve farm life. There was a demand for "how-to" agriculture books. *The Modern Horse Doctor* sold 50,000 copies, *Youatt and Martin On Cattle* over 20,000 copies. Many agricultural journals were started in a period of 20 years beginning in 1819 when the *American Farmer* was first published in Baltimore. By 1850, it's estimated there were 60 journals devoted almost exclusively to agriculture and horticulture, with an aggregate circulation of around 550,000, indicating a new spirit of inquiry among farmers.

Among these journals were the *New England Farmer*, *The Genesee Farmer*, the *Rural New-Yorker* and *The American Agriculturist*, established in 1842, whose circulation rose to 180,000 in less than 15 years. *The American Agriculturist* is still being published today.

Farmers used the "letters to the editor" as an audience for their age-old complaints, as evidenced by the following letter to the *Rural New-Yorker*:

"For the benefit of those who are inclined to envy the independence and prosperity of the farmer, I give you herewith a detailed statement of the 'outgo' and 'income' of ten acres, which I fallowed and sowed to wheat. Not that I desire to discourage anyone, but simply to show that the picture of 'farm life' as generally seen through agricultural journals, has like all others, another side to it."

[It would appear that J.S.W.'s 43-bushel harvest was a virtual crop failure — which has been a risk throughout the history of agriculture.]

The *New England Farmer* for June of 1849 presents the ideal farmhouse. They reported that "According to the carpenter's estimate a farm cottage in this style, extremely furnished in a neat and thorough manner would cost about $3,000 in this vicinity (Massachusetts). Where labor and materials are cheaper it could be built for $1,500 to $2,000 according to the style of finish."

| June | Plowing, harrowing and rolling, 8½ days at .................. | $3.50 | $29.75 |
|---|---|---|---|
| June | 143 loads manure, at ............... | .60 | 85.80 |
| June | Loading & spreading do., 9 d's ....... | 1.75 | 15.75 |
| July | Gang-plowing & har'ing, 3½ d's ...... | 3.50 | 12.25 |
| Sept. | Plowing & pulverizing, 11 d's at ...... | 3.50 | 38.50 |
| Sept. | 18 bush, Diehl wheat, at ............ | 1.75 | 31.50 |
| Sept. | Drilling and ditching, 1½ d's, at ...... | 3.50 | 5.25 |
| July | Harvesting 10 acres, at ............. | 1.75 | 17.50 |
| Sept. | Threshing and mulching ........... | | 11.95 |
| | Total | | $248.25 |

Income

| | 43 bush. white wheat, at ............ | 1.45 | 62.35 |
|---|---|---|---|
| | Total | | $189.90 |

Board is included in the above rates.
Suspension Bridge, N.Y.,                J.S.W.

As the soil wore out from lack of fertilization on the Eastern Seaboard the farmers left the old ground behind. By 1850 one traveler wrote: "Eastern Virginia appeared to have suffered the ravages of a great war or an attack by another horseman of the Apocalypse. I travelled for 50 miles on horseback and could find nothing but abandoned farms and plantations with buildings in decay and fields overgrown

Robert Bailey Thomas started the *Farmer's Almanack* in 1792 in Sterling, Massachusetts. It still gives planting and weather advice to farmers. The competing *Albany Almanac* in 1847 used woodcuts to suggest new trends in agriculture. For the month of March a new fence building technique was introduced. The rails were inserted in notched posts, instead of being stacked zigzag. For the month of April, the *Almanac* advocated distributing barnyard manure on the fields. This was a revolutionary idea in most areas where farmers sometimes moved their barns to a new location to rid the barnyard of manure. Moon phases were important for the planting of crops.

A scene of desolation prevailed in many areas where the soil had worn out.

with nettles and brush. Mother Nature is reclaiming that which for 200 years has been giving food and clothing to man."

Edmund Ruffin, who began advocating better management of the soil in 1821, headed a reform movement in southern agriculture. Publishing essays and speaking to groups of farmers, Ruffin suggested the use of marl, manure and other fertilizers after taking a correct chemical analysis of the soil. He later founded the progressive *Farmer's Register* in 1833. Through his influence, attempts were made at bringing large areas of southern soil back into production.

In 1840, Liebig reported on the progress of agriculture to the British Association for the Advance of Science. He opened a new world of thought on applying chemical investigations to the soil. Liebig said, "To manure an acre of land with 40 pounds of bone dust is sufficient to supply three crops of wheat, clover, potatoes, turnips, etc., with phosphates. The more finely the bones are reduced to powder and the more intimately they are mixed with the soil, the more easy they are assimilated. The most easy and practical mode of effecting their division is to pour over the bones in the state of fine powder, half of their weight in sulphuric acid diluted with three or four parts of water." Liebig opened the way for a whole system of soil fertilization which has extended into modern times.

Previously, the farmer had confined himself to the use of either a compost of animal manure or vegetable materials — if he used any fertilizer at all.

Through other investigations came the discovery of the value of guano (bird dung) as a fertilizer. Guano became so popular that by 1851, 800,000 tons had been imported into the United States and by 1856, 2,000,000 tons were imported at a value of over $1.2 million.

Raw bone, super phosphate of lime, ground and crushed bone, fish guano and rendering company manure and offal also found a strong market. These early efforts to improve the soil laid the foundation for today's fertilizer industry.

Edmund Ruffin

# IV
# More Than
# Lip Service

## 1851-1870

Henry L. Ellsworth

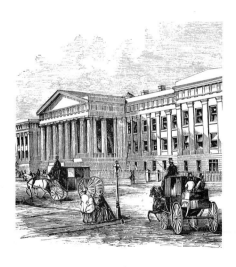

The Patent Office began to collect agricultural information and statistics in 1836.

The country and the agricultural industry were coming of age. The scientific discoveries, mechanical inventions, general spirit of inquiry, and the increasing awareness of the American people brought new direction to agriculture.

Alfalfa was grown on the West Coast, and the winter-hardy Grimm alfalfa was introduced. Purebred cattle — Herefords, Ayrshires, Galloways, Jerseys, Devons and Holsteins — were imported and bred. The first poultry exhibition was held in the United States.

The Corn Belt was stabilizing in its present area and wheat occupied the newer and cheaper land west of the corn areas. Wisconsin and Illinois were the chief wheat states during the early 1860s. The Cotton Belt moved westward.

The frontier jumped the Great Plains and the Rockies from the Mississippi River to the Pacific Coast. Expanded market demand spurred improved technology and increases in farm production.

Along with the agricultural progress came the government's awareness that the needs of this important industry were changing. Congress wanted to get involved in promoting the best interests of agriculture. The question was how.

Proposals for an agricultural branch of government were made as early as 1776 by President Washington. It wasn't until 1836, however, that positive action was actually taken in this direction.

At that time Commissioner of Patents Henry L. Ellsworth took it upon himself to distribute seeds he obtained abroad to enterprising American farmers. In reporting his work to Congress, he suggested that the federal government should make greater provisions for agricultural interests.

Three years later Congress appropriated $1,000 of Patent Office fees for collecting agricultural statistics, conducting agricultural investigations and distributing seeds.

Under Ellsworth's direction, the Patent Office conducted experiments with imported species of plants and collected information concerning crops, weather, rainfall, plant diseases, exports and farm machinery. The data were published in an annual report by the Commissioner of Patents and farmers sup-

plemented the report with accounts of their experiences.

After 1845 politics interfered with the agricultural work of the Patent Office. The quality of their reports declined. The free seeds which had been imported brought new diseases and harmful insects with them.

Farm editors, agricultural leaders and officers of numerous county and state agricultural societies weren't very happy with the work of the agricultural division of the Patent Office. They wanted their own separate agency.

The movement gathered momentum when the United States Agricultural Society was established in 1851. Its major goal was enactment of legislation establishing a separate agricultural agency. In 1860, the Republican Party adopted a platform for agrarian reform which included the creation of a separate Department of Agriculture.

When Abraham Lincoln was elected President on the Republican ticket, the drive accelerated. In his first message to Congress, President Lincoln called on the lawmakers to pass legislation establishing a Department of Agriculture. The turning point came when the South seceded from the Union. At this time most

Crossing the plains and mountains.

John Francis Appleby invented the basic knotter in 1858 while working on his father's farm in Wisconsin. The invention became the foundation for all farm binding machinery.

President Lincoln and his cabinet initiated several pieces of legislation that would benefit the development of agriculture in the country.

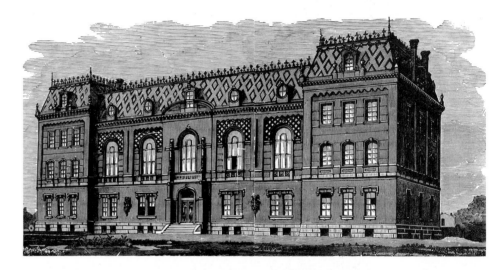

The first Department of Agriculture building had a 5-acre plot that was used for testing and experimenting with various crops.

Isaac Newton, the first Commissioner of Agriculture, seated center, with principal staff members.

of Congress supported legislation setting up the department. Its only opposition came from a few conservatives, and some people who felt it wasn't necessary to pay lip service to farm interests. A few were also concerned that other economic blocs didn't have separate departments promoting their interests. This argument didn't weigh heavily on Congress, however, as they realized that agriculture was the country's most important industry and affected the lives of everyone.

The House and Senate passed the legislation overwhelmingly and on May 15, 1862, President Lincoln signed the bill which created the independent Department of Agriculture, headed by a commissioner.

Lincoln appointed Isaac Newton of Pennsylvania as the first Commissioner of Agriculture. Newton was not well-known but had some agricultural experience and close political ties to Lincoln. His administration was marred by frequent criticism from agricultural leaders, farm editors and legislators. Nonetheless, he managed to hire people who turned out a good deal of noteworthy research. The department initiated chemical analysis of soils and crops, started cataloging insects, revived statistical work and published a number of worthwhile reports.

Newton, who died in office in 1866, played an important role in getting the new department off to a fairly successful start. In 1889, the department was elevated to the cabinet status it enjoys today.

**The Homestead Act of 1862 was seen as the logical culmination of a long struggle by the pioneer farmers for freer access to public land.**

Another significant piece of agricultural legislation to glide through the Congress of 1862 was the Homestead Act. This law made available 160 acres of public domain to every American citizen who was the head of a family or over 21 years of age. The individual could obtain a patent to the land after residing on it for five years and making improvements. Only a nominal registration fee was required. Full title to the land could be gained after six months of actual residence if the individual paid $1.25 an acre.

The Homestead Act of 1862 was seen as the logical culmination of a long struggle by the pioneer farmers for freer access to public land. Southern congressmen had opposed previous bills of this nature because they thought the legislation would stimulate settlement in the Northwest and upset the balance between the free and slave states.

The Homestead Act was part of President Lincoln's platform for agrarian reform. Like the bill setting up the Department of Agriculture, this legislation was easily enacted when the southern representatives withdrew from Congress.

The Homestead Act served as a symbol of American democracy to native-borns and immigrants. By the end of the Civil War it was contributing to the further rapid growth of the West and the development of family-sized farms.

A third area in which the Congress of 1862 distinguished itself as a champion of agriculture was in its support of the establishment of an agricultural and mechanical college in each state. This bill, the Morrill Land-Grant College Act, was signed into law in July of 1862. The act provided for a grant of 30,000 acres of land, or its equivalent in scrip, to the individual states for each representative and senator they had in Congress. The land was to be used as endowment for the support of a college of agriculture and mechanics. The grants ranged in size from 90,000 acres for Delaware, Florida, Kansas, Nebraska and Nevada to 990,000 acres for New York.

This legislation came about as agricultural leaders all over the country saw an increasing need for agricultural education.

Pennsylvania State University was established as an early land-grant college. Students tilled the ground in front of Old Main to gain practical experience.

Sadly, many farmers in the United States were not considering new ideas or improved methods. They seemed to believe that the soil and supply of new land was inexhaustible. They were preoccupied with immediate returns, and simply moved when the soil became depleted.

European educators and researchers joined American agricultural leaders in urging U.S. farmers to learn more about sound methods. When insects and animal diseases became serious, American farmers began to understand the importance of furthering their agricultural education.

The principle of the Morrill Act was not new. Government aid to education was deeply rooted in the American way of life. The Land Ordinance of 1785 reserved one section of land in each township of a territory for the establishment of public schools. It also provided two townships, or a total of 46,080 acres, to each state for the establishment of a seminary of learning or a university.

Opponents of the Morrill Land-Grant College Act questioned its constitutionality. Principal author Justin S. Morrill of Ver-

Northern farmers piled hay on top of their small barns, and constructed a cover-up with eight wooden posts and a wooden roof. This did a fair job of protecting the hay and insulating the barn from winter's weather hazards.

Women and children worked the land while the men fought the Civil War.

mont was quick to point out that the farmers were the least privileged group as far as government handouts or aids were concerned. They deserved enactment of this legislation. Even those members of Congress who believed in strict interpretation of the federal constitution, though opposed to granting direct financial aid, thought the government could give land for education.

Due to the Civil War and to a lack of experienced instructors in agriculture, the land-grant colleges were slow in getting started.

In the years since their establishment, the land-grant colleges have become the focal points of scientific research, collegiate training and adult education in agriculture. The government's action gave stimulus and some degree of leadership to the education and improved agricultural practices of the American farmer.

Prior to the Civil War, cotton was king in the South, with much of it produced on plantations by slave labor. The significant fact about cotton culture with slave labor was that it had to constantly go on to fresh land in order to be profitable. If the great planters were to prosper, they had to move further west with their slaves when their lands became worn out or too expensive.

This situation prompted settlement beyond the Mississippi River and brought about the admission of Missouri as a slave state in 1821. The same need for new land was one of the causes leading to the annexation of Texas. Observers expected cotton growing to spread way to California, but a lack of rainfall prevented further westward movement.

The large southern plantation owners were a minority. Only

After the hay was cut, farmers forked it into piles before hoisting it up onto a horse-drawn hay rack.

The cotton crop of 1870 exceeded those of previous years. In the aftermath of
the Civil War, two systems of labor were adopted in the South: hiring and
working on shares. (Sharecropping became an important part of southern
agriculture and remained so until after World War II.) Some plantation owners
gave one-third of the crop and food to the hands. Others gave one-half of the
crop and the hands fed themselves. A gentleman from West Tennessee
reported: "With cotton at even less than 15 cents [a pound], I will make fully
20 percent on the entire value of my plantation and stock this year and I never
made 6 percent before the War. I don't have any worry with it. I only need to
ride over it once a month." The editors of *Hearth and Home* for 1870
conceded that: "In a trip through every cotton state except Texas and
Arkansas, we could not find a man who had adopted this system
[sharecropping] who did not expect to make money, even with present prices.
Those plantation owners who are using hired labor are only living from hand
to mouth and will certainly go bankrupt."

about seven percent of the landowners had more than 50 slaves and cultivated more than 500 acres. The smaller farmers produced general crops and livestock, and eked out a living with some cotton and tobacco.

In the North, there were small farms everywhere. Almost all were worked by their owners, who raised a variety of crops. In order to make the best use of their land, many northern farmers began to fertilize, buy new machinery and pay attention to the raising of stock.

During the war, when the men joined the Union and Confederate armies, many of the farms in both the North and South were run by women and children. They were anxious to do "the men's work" in the fields. One girl who was binding grain said, "I tell Mother that as long as the country can't get along without grain, nor the army without food, we're serving the country just as much here in the harvest field as our boys are on the battlefield — and that sort o' takes the edge off this business of doing men's work, you know."

A missionary living in Kansas wrote that he saw the wife of one of his parishioners driving the team behind a reaper while her husband was at Vicksburg. He wrote, "With what help she can secure and the assistance of her little children, she is carrying on the farm."

But northern and southern farmers faced a lot of hardships when the war ended. The farmers of the North had experienced great prosperity during the war, but now faced reduced demands for their products at a time when their production was on the increase. Prices paid for farm products dropped. In the South, the problem was more severe. The war had demoralized southern farmers. Their one-crop system had drastically reduced soil fertility. And they were heavily in debt.

After the Civil War hundreds of thousands of immigrants began pouring into the country. Many of these helped to settle the West. Ships like these carried the immigrants to U.S. shores and returned to Europe laden with grain.

The war had overshadowed the important accomplishments of the Congress of 1862. Legislation creating the Department of Agriculture, the Homestead Act, the Morrill Land-Grant College Act and liberal aid for the building of a railroad to the Pacific were extremely important to the development of agriculture and expansion of the West. Thousands of war-weary young men could establish themselves as farmers under the favorable terms of the Homestead Act. They traveled to the fertile prairie lands, and set themselves up in wheat production.

This period in American history marked the time when progress and development would be charted in cooperation with the policies and funds of the federal government.

# V
# Taking Stock

## 1871-1880

"The West is a total wasteland" was a concept that started to disappear after the Reconstruction. Thousands of immigrants from Europe flocked to the new West. Scandinavian immigrants streamed in, settling on the Eastern Shore and in what is now the Upper Midwest.

While most settlers traveled westward by wagon before 1870, railroad expansion made it easier for farmers to reach unoccupied land after that date. The Northern Pacific was completed to Moorhead, Minnesota, on the Red River in 1871; the Burlington reached Kearney, Nebraska, where it made connections with the Union Pacific in 1872; the Santa Fe arrived at Emporia, Kansas, in 1870 and was built westward to the Colorado line two years later. The Missouri, Kansas and Texas arrived at the northern boundary of Indian Territory (Oklahoma) in March, 1871. Many shorter railroad and branch lines spread out from the main line centers.

East finally met West with the joining of the first railroad line. It was now possible to travel from the Eastern Shore to California. The golden spike was driven at Promontory Point, Utah, on May 10, 1869.

The influx of new homesteaders did not please the range cattle industry. The cattlemen had converted the five-hundred-mile-wide strip east of the Rockies from Mexico to Canada from a buffalo range to the world's greatest cattle pasture. No fences here!

The range cattle industry had begun in the 1690s when Spanish missionaries introduced longhorn cattle into the Southwest. Longhorns, numbering six million head in 1865, were the foundation stock for Texas herds. Cattle were driven from Texas to new ranges and to the railheads in the Kansas area for shipment to the East.

The business of herding the longhorn was the most picturesque that agriculture affords. It produced the western cowboy, who typified the free frontier spirit and whose peculiar costume was borrowed in part from the Mexican herdsman.

He wore the leather breeches (chaparajos), often covered on the front with wool, the broad sombrero, and the Cuban-style high-heeled boots, and was fond of Mexican decorations on his bridle bit and spurs.

After weeks or months of lonely life on the plains, the cowboy was apt to lose his self-restraint in a frontier town. He gambled and drank heavily; sometimes in an alcoholic frenzy he "shot up the town", often with more noise than damage. Every now and then some fellow cowboy or the gambler who had "wronged" him felt the force of his bullets.

Grassland was free and open to any person who could buy cattle and hire cowboys to guard them. A group of these "cow-punchers" built a log cabin and stayed on the range during the winter, while the cattle roamed at large.

Herds belonging to different owners became mixed, so there was a spring roundup for branding the calves. Each owner sent one or more cowboys to each of the roundups to protect his interest. A camp outfit stocked with provisions was taken to the roundup site. From here, the men set out on their horses every morning, riding many miles, driving the cattle to a central point from all directions. In the afternoon the cowboys rode into the herd they had collected, and cut out or separated the cows with calves that belonged to their respective employers. When a group was separated from the herd, the calves were roped with a lasso, thrown and then branded with hot irons.

The work was extremely hard. A man used two or three horses a day, and had ten or more in his remuda. The horses rested, but there was little rest for the men during the two or three months of the roundup. Besides being in the saddle from daybreak until dark, they took turns guarding the herd at night.

The work was not only difficult, but dangerous. Horses were often as wild as the cattle. Their bucking, while it furnished entertainment for the bystanders, sometimes resulted in serious

"He wore leather breeches . . . the broad sombrero and the Cuban-styled high-heeled boots."

Breaking camp after the roundup.

The bunkhouse.

40-mule redeye, the potent beverage served in local saloons, was reported to have the kick of 40 mules, leaving the consumers with red eyes.

injury to the rider.

The most trying and dangerous part of a cowboy's life came when the cattle stampeded. Day or night, the cowboys had to follow and head off the leaders. After the herd had calmed down, the men often searched many square miles to find the scattered animals.

The extension of railroads into the Far West helped make stock raising a more profitable business. In 1878, cattle on the range were worth $8.00 a head; a few years later they were worth $12.00, and within 5 years they rose to more than $20.00 in some places. Shorthorns and Herefords were brought to the West, improving the quality of the stock and providing the foundation for today's fine beef.

The success of this romantic industry, however, was doomed. As pioneers moved into the West, the 160-acre plots they settled

Cattlemen in Texas and the Southwest used the Chisholm, Pawnee and Abilene trails as a pipeline for supplying cattle to railheads and shipment east. The trail rider herded the longhorn approximately 12 miles a day.

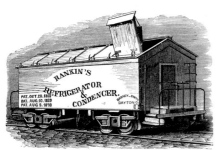

Mr. T.L. Rankin of Osage County, Kansas, patented his refrigerator car in 1868. Meat shipped to New York via the Kansas Pacific Railroad reached New York in 14 days in 1872. Twelve iceboxes or chests were arranged on the top of the car. Each was independent of the other and closed on a rubber sheet to "keep each ice chest air tight".

under the Homestead Act were often part of a cattleman's range. This presented a problem for the cattlemen because 160 acres just weren't enough. Although some took advantage of the Homestead Act by having each of their cowboys take a tract of 160 acres, or filing claims of that amount for a number of "dummy" homesteaders, the new settlers were choking the cattle industry as it existed.

Tension mounted. Sometimes a frontier farmer would be driven off by reckless cattlemen who considered that they had first rights to the land. The extreme was a shoot-out between rancher and farmer. The average cattleman, however, had no incentive to protect his range. He overstocked and overgrazed. This, combined with the homesteaders, left the cattle industry in a vulnerable position. Finally, low prices and bad weather helped end the open range livestock business.

Stockmen began to acquire land, drilled wells, built water storage reservoirs and fenced everything in.

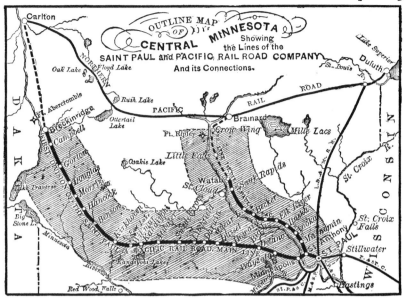
Congress granted land to the railroads to encourage their westward expansion. The railroads promoted settlement of their land, as well as land still available under the Homestead Act. Advertisements appeared in publications in the U.S. and abroad.

Newly arrived immigrants took advantage of the railroad in moving to the West. After arrival on the docks of New York they were transported to the railroad station, and then carried west to take up claim on plots of land.

The Journal of the American Agricultural Association carried an ad for barb wire in its first edition, published in 1881.

Joe F. Glidden invented the Glidden steel barbed wire fence. He was granted a patent on it in May, 1874. The fencing material was made by "coiling a short piece of wire between its ends around the fence wire."

A retail hardware operator in De Kalb, Illinois, I.L. Ellwood, formed a partnership with Glidden and began the manufacture of barbed wire fencing.

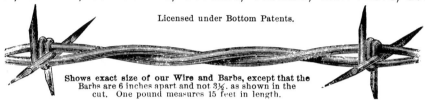

Glidden barbed wire was manufactured at I.L. Ellwood & Co.

The new breed of western farmers couldn't rely on extensive forests to supply lumber for rail fences, as the eastern and mid-western farmers had done. Their fields weren't full of rocks, so they couldn't build sturdy stone fences, as was done in the East and Midwest. They needed a strong, inexpensive fencing material to protect their homesteads.

**B**arbed wire made fencing on a large scale possible. It met all of the tests. It was strong; the wind didn't blow it down. Its sharp, pointed barbs kept cattle from pushing it over. And it was cheap.

The range industry divided its domain into summer- and winter-grazing areas. The stockmen cut meadow grass for hay. They developed better cattle by selective breeding.

For the homesteader of this area, the principal crop was wheat. These families had only a few head of cattle, hogs or horses. The Kansas-Nebraska-Dakotas-Minnesota-area farmers turned to raising wheat because it could be grown quickly and easily. It stored well, and there was a ready market.

While most of the farms were small, there were a few "bonanza" spreads in the Dakotas. These farms had as many as 10,000 acres planted in wheat. Eastern and foreign money was poured into these operations. They received a lot of attention from the press, stimulated national interest in the region, but made up only a minor part of the farm population.

Strangely, the wheat farmers of the West faced the same problems the tobacco and cotton farmers did in the South. They failed to recognize the negative effect of producing the same crop for many years in succession on the same piece of land. Soon, their land yielded only one-half or one-third of what it had before. As the wheat belt moved on, it left in its wake worn-out fields that required more careful tillage and greater attention to more varied and scientific agriculture.

One good result came from the misfortunes of the wheat growers: farmers began to study the causes of their problems.

All through prior American history the increase of farm crops came chiefly from the use of new land. The American farmer was a miner, rather than a farmer; he extracted valuable materials from the earth without putting anything back. The general ideas of scientific farming were held by many men as early as Washington's time and before; but there were three obstacles to their being put into practice by the average American farmer.

First, it was easier, and generally more profitable to cultivate new land than to do intensive farming on the old. Secondly, even the most intelligent farmers had little knowledge of the proper treatment of soils and plant life. The scientists themselves didn't know a lot about such matters. And third, the pioneer's independent nature made him hesitate to develop new ideas as they came along. To do that would be "book farming" and not practical. The

"As a display of the productions of forest, field, furnace and mine, as well as the fold and the stall, the collection gathered on the fairgrounds was in every way excellent," said the *Hearth and Home* of the 1871 St. Louis Fair. The fair brought together the finest collection of horses, cattle, sheep and hogs "ever gathered". Almost 20 acres were covered with agricultural implements. Household articles were on display. The best of crops raised all over the country had been gathered. Many prizes were given out for excellence, and the 100,000 people who attended learned a lot about progressive agricultural practices.

Farming the land was a tedious task.

Women worked carding, spinning and weaving to provide clothing for the family.

Upon settling in the New World, immigrant groups often raised specialty crops and helped each other in the harvesting. Many German immigrants raised hops for use in brewing beer.

pioneer was succeeding in a new country and in the midst of hard, adverse circumstances, primarily by taking care of himself. His chief pride was his self-reliance.

By the late 1800s these attitudes began to change. The government's supply of good quality free land was being exhausted, and farmers soon realized that it was necessary to practice better farming methods: that agriculture based on tradition, custom and superstition must go. Research by colleges of agriculture and by the state and federal departments of agriculture was providing great quantities of useful scientific knowledge about soils, plants and animals.

The push for this so-called scientific revolution came from

many sources. Agricultural fairs became important instructional media. The land-grant colleges educated young people and encouraged the application of practical ideas through farmer institutes.

Many forward-looking individuals of the day believed an agricultural college ought to do more than merely preach the knowledge that men already had about farming. College should be, they felt, a place where new knowledge is constantly being discovered. This could only come about by conducting experiments. The first separate state agricultural experiment station was set up in Connecticut in 1875. Within a few years a number of states followed.

The greatest step in this direction came in 1887, when Congress passed the Hatch Act. This law appropriated money for experiment stations in connection with the various agricultural

The first agricultural experiment station.

colleges. These stations conducted investigations, made experiments in all fields of agriculture, and published reports.

Agricultural experiment station work led to important discoveries, not only for agriculture but for the benefit of all humankind. For example, one station tried to find out why their dairy cows were internally bleeding and dying. They traced the prob-

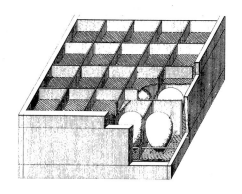

The egg transporting case was patented in 1873. Divided into squares to hold just one egg, the brown pasteboard layers were packed into a wooden box for easy handling.

THE PREMIUM BRONZED TURKEY.

PORTRAIT OF A CROSS OF GUINEA FOWL AND TURKEY,

THE PRIZE TRIO OF BUFF COCHINS, OWNED BY ISAAC VAN WINKLE, Esq., GREENVILLE, N. J.
[Drawn by A. Hochstein and Engraved Expressly for Moore's Rural New-Yorker.]

"No one seems to make egg producing a specialty, with a single eye to making a living out of it," said the *Rural New Yorker* in 1871. And it went on to suggest that because of an excellent source of supply of food — that of scraps from hotels and restaurants — New York and other large cities would be good places to establish "egg manufactories". The New York State Poultry Show broke attendance records in December of 1871. Poultry husbandry was becoming more of a science. The Premium Bronzed turkey was said to "weigh the heaviest, fatten the most rapidly and be reared with much less trouble than any other variety". These turkeys were a cross between the domestic and the wild and the foundation for the modern turkey enterprise. The cross between the guinea fowl and the turkey that was introduced at the show was said to be a noble bird in carriage and appearance. "Popular taste" it was thought would make this bird a favorite. But that didn't happen. The Buff Cochins won the American Agriculturists Cup.

lem to a spoiled substance in sweet clover hay. This work led to the discovery of dicoumarin. It also provided the basis for the discovery of warfarin, a blood anti-coagulant used in rat poison. Dicoumarin is used today to treat arterial thrombosis, or blood clots.

Streptomycin was developed at Rutgers University, the Babcock butterfat test at the University of Wisconsin, fundamental work on transistors and the first television tubes at Purdue, the cyclotron at the University of California and hybrid corn in Connecticut and Illinois.

A major factor advancing the cause of scientific agriculture was the birth of agricultural organizations. Farmers began to organize in order to fight for their interests and to oppose the influences of large corporations, the railroads and city politicians. Among their organizational goals was increased agricultural education for their members.

**Farmers began to organize in order to fight for their interests**

The most prominent early organization formed to support the farmers' cause was the Patrons of Husbandry, or the Grange. Oliver Hudson Kelley is regarded as the father of the Grange movement. In 1866 he was authorized by Isaac Newton, the first Commissioner of Agriculture, to make a survey of the farm conditions in the South following the Civil War. During this time, Kelley conceived the idea of a fraternal organization composed of farmers from all sections of the country. Together with six other men and his niece, Carolyn A. Hall, Kelley framed a ritual and constitution for the organization which was ratified on December 4, 1867.

Kelley resigned his position with the Department of Agriculture to establish the new organization. On April 16, 1868, he instituted Fredonia Grange No.1 in western New York. In 1869 the first State Grange came into existence in Minnesota. The following year saw similar organizations founded in Illinois, Indiana and Ohio. Two years later there were State Granges in 25 states. By the close of 1872, over a thousand local chapters had been established.

The original purpose of the Patrons of Husbandry was to improve farm life. They hoped to lighten the farmers' burdens, and to create better feelings between the farmers of the North and South.

Fredonia Grange No. 1 was the first
Grange organization to be established.

Oliver Hudson Kelley was the founder of the Grange. His niece, Carolyn Hall, was an extremely important influence on her uncle. She helped him establish the framework for the Grange.

The Grange wanted to advance education in all branches of agriculture. Lecturers went out to discuss not only agricultural problems but also other questions of the day. The study of agriculture was encouraged and prizes were offered for outstanding production.

The Grange was also a social fraternity of both men and women, with secret rituals and a series of degrees.

As it became better organized, it promoted cooperative buying and selling. The Grange bought machinery, bags and twine in large quantities from the manufacturers at low prices for local member distribution. It sold and shipped produce directly to the commission merchants in large cities and received higher prices by eliminating the middleman.

Eventually the Grange organized politically, especially to lobby for railroad regulations. Gradually, it declined as a political force and membership dropped. After 1885 it discontinued many of its economic activities. It continued as a social and fraternal order concentrating on various educational projects. In the early 1900s the group grew in influence once again. In 1919 the Grange established a legislative headquarters in Washington, D.C. and is still active in governmental affairs.

A drawing from a popular farm publication in 1870.

THE FARM

AS IT WAS.

AS IT WILL BE.

# VI
# Home Sweet Home

## 1881-1900

Farmers have always carried on a love affair with the land.

Unlike the hunter, fur trapper and cowboy who have captivated the public in legendary folklore, the farmer is the forgotten character of the American frontier. But he was the true harbinger of advancing civilization.

It was the farmer who carried civilization with him in his wagon. His purpose was to build in the West a model of the society he had known in the East. As he moved he left in his wake abundant farms, growing villages, roads, canals and railroads. Schools, libraries and theaters were among the symbols of his maturing social order.

When farmers started their march following the Civil War, the Far West with the exception of California was virtually unsettled. Between the Pacific Coast and the Missouri River, there were only isolated settlements in Nevada, Utah, Colorado and other distant spots. As the farmers' march slowed at the end of the century, the entire West was occupied, except for the mountains and the deserts.

Between 1870 and 1900 more land was settled and placed under cultivation by farmers than in all the prior history of the continent.

With all this land under cultivation, farmers started to encounter new situations. Lack of rainfall became a major problem. When settlers first moved into the Great Plains between 1875 and 1886, the rainfall was abundant. But later the climate fluctuated between drought, abundant rainfall and scanty rainfall. These fluctuations just weren't expected and farmers didn't know how to cope with them.

Because of uncertain rainfall, the plains farmer needed feed and cash reserves to get over periods of drought and crop failure.

This meant raising the right grain crops and relying heavily on livestock. Adopting new farming practices, such as summer fallowing, was important to his success. It was crucial he choose crop strains that would produce best under minimum moisture conditions.

In 1889 Hardy Webster Campbell devised a system of "dry farming". His method was to conserve the scant moisture supply in the soil by reducing or eliminating runoff and evaporation, and by increasing absorption and retention of moisture by the soil. Campbell invented a "subsoil packer" in 1890. His theory

Hardy Webster Campbell devised systems for dry farming in 1889.

51

H.G.— Put on your weight, Patrick; put on your weight! The moisture is there, and I'm going down deeper to find it!
Patrick — Be jabers! me weight is all on! (*Solil.* – This is a quare counthry!)

One method Campbell espoused was deep plowing. According to this cartoon which appeared in an 1889 agricultural journal, all farmers were not convinced of its success.

was that if the subsoil was packed, water would be attracted from lower depths by capillary action. A "dust mulch" on top protected the surface from evaporation and he urged that this be renewed after each rainfall.

Other techniques that Campbell believed were necessary for successful dry farming included deep fall plowing, light seeding and alternating summer fallow with tillage. Other proponents of dry farming advocated planting only those crops adapted to dry conditions.

The practice of dry farming didn't really impress the area farmers. But the railroads liked it. The Northern Pacific railroad hired Campbell to operate five demonstration farms in North Dakota. He delivered twenty lectures along the route of the Denver railroad line. Eventually he supervised 43 farms in five states, and his work received national attention.

The Dry Farming Congress was formed to promote the concept and was the sounding board of optimism. They held seminars in several communities in the northern Great Plains and invited commercial, real estate, government and technical people. But only a very few farmers participated in the meetings.

Department of Agriculture officials were concerned about the oversimplification of dry farming. Proponents made the practice sound like a new, original method, when it really wasn't.

Dry farming was practiced in many western states through the 1920s. Its importance to the West was not so much as a system of farming, but rather as a promotional tool to settle this semiarid region.

An altogether sound practice did emerge from this period. When America was discovered, the Spanish explorers in what is now New Mexico and Arizona, found the Pueblo Indians had maintained a fairly sophisticated irrigation system.

The first settlers to use irrigation in agriculture were the Mormons, in Utah, in 1847. When they arrived at Great Salt Lake, they immediately began to plant food crops for the coming winter. But a white crust of alkali covered the ground, which was baked so hard it broke their plows. Sagebrush and bunchgrass were the only signs of vegetation, except for the small trees which grew along the few stream beds. The Mormons probably had never seen irrigation practiced or even heard of it. But an

The Mormons in Utah made the desert bloom.

ingenious member of the band suggested damming a nearby creek and allowing the water to spread and soften the soil. At the same time they watered the newly planted seed.

The grain didn't develop that year; it was a late season. But their potatoes grew, so the Mormons were furnished with seed for the next spring's planting.

While gold mining was hardly an agricultural enterprise, the California mines were more valuable than people thought. The water trickling from the sluice prompted green growth and showed that vegetation would grow in a desert, if properly wa-

Ditches and sluices abandoned by the miners of the 1849 gold rush were used for the first attempt at irrigation in Colorado. The water coming down Pike's Peak was directed onto the arid lands.

tered. Enterprising farmers soon realized great profits from the sale of the vegetables to the well-paid miners — vegetables watered from the same water that washed over the nuggets and gold dust in the sluice.

Greeley, Colorado, possibly owes its beginning to irrigation. In 1869, Nathan C. Meeker, who was then with the *New York Tribune*, was encouraged by Horace Greeley, ("Go West, young man!") the editor of the paper, to carry out a plan for making a settlement in Colorado. Soon a number of eastern men and their families came and founded the Union Colony of Colorado.

The colony owned the land; each person had a village lot and bought a farm from the colony. The proceeds of these sales were used to build public facilities — a school, library, town hall, etc. At first there were hard times; blizzards and locusts almost wiped out the community. One of the settlers summed up their plight: "Some of us were pretty well pegged out in the contest and some of us were already dead."

Horace Greeley, the editor of the New York Tribune, encouraged the settlement of the town that bears his name in Colorado.

But these were persistent pioneers, with high ideals of home and community. The people built and owned an irrigation system. They found that their soil would produce the best of potatoes in quantities that yielded large profits. Alfalfa was planted and a plow was developed to turn it over. Moved by

At noon on April 22, 1889, a gunshot signaled the availability of land in Oklahoma. A great crowd dashed across the line in a mad race for the best lands and town lots. The entire region was settled almost within a day. Guthrie was one of the communities that sprang up.

Expanded railways were important to the marketing of farm products.

Mechanical corn binders gathered the corn into bundles which were then shocked. This cut down on the labor required for harvesting corn.

The development of the manure spreader encouraged greater utilization of this valuable fertilizer.

Grain harvesters moved across the enormous grain fields of the Northwest like an army of ants. Twenty-eight horse hitches were needed to pull the huge harvesters.

Greeley's success others founded agricultural communities in neighboring counties.

The beginnings of irrigation in Utah, California and Colorado demonstrated unbelievable potential. With plenty of sunshine and a never-failing supply of water always under control, grains, fruits and vegetables grew surprisingly well.

Despite these isolated successes with irrigation, however, western members of Congress realized that easy and inexpensive methods of diverting water were limited. On March 3, 1877, Congress passed the Desert Land Act, whereby a farmer could claim up to a section of land if he promised to irrigate it. This law, however, didn't prove to be much help to those who were interested in irrigation. The governors of Washington, Wyoming, Idaho, Arizona and New Mexico reported agricultural successes, but needed storage facilities for irrigation water in order to make good use of their land.

The Cary Act of 1894 granted each arid state up to a million acres of land to be sold at 50¢ an acre, the receipts to be used for irrigation work. This act did not work well either, because the land simply didn't sell in any quantity.

**The Reclamation Act of 1902 also represented a significant change in American land policy.**

A genuine boost for irrigation came when Congress passed the Reclamation Act in 1902. Under this system, the government sold land in any of the states in the Far West and the proceeds were put into a fund that was spent for building irrigation systems. The farmers, either by purchase or under the Homestead law, could then take up land that could be reached by water. When such an irrigation system went into operation, the farmers were to pay back the government in ten annual payments, an amount that would finally equal the cost of the system. The money would be reinvested in another project for another locality.

The Reclamation Act of 1902 also represented a significant change in American land policy. It was specifically designed for irrigable land in the West. It provided money without interest, and represented more government participation.

The first construction under the provisions of this act was the Salt River project in Arizona, served by the Roosevelt Dam. The Hoover, the Grand Coulee and Bonneville dams in the Northwest, and the Shasta and Friant dams in California were added later. By 1915, 25 projects had been initiated under the Reclamation Act, representing an investment of more than 80 million dollars by the federal government.

The farmers of the New Mexico area grew a variety of grains in 1888, as well as vegetables, garden products, fruits (especially grapes) and some semitropical fruits. Beef and sheep breeds were improving, but the market for them was bad.

However, only 12 years later the territorial governor was able to report: "No business offers more profitable returns than does sheep raising and wool growing in New Mexico." Vast im-

By 1890 all of the machinery that would require horsepower had been invented. From here on, entrepreneurs would concentrate their efforts on mechanically-powered machines.

Barn raising had been an important community activity since colonial times.

The sodhouse frontier extended from Kansas to the Dakotas. Houses were built partly underground with the walls made from squares of sod. Prairie grass was used for roofing and the settlers burned dried cow and buffalo chips for fuel. For those more fortunate farmers who were able to build houses of wood, sod made a good insulation against the winter winds.

A large hired labor force was used to harvest many crops. Wisconsin cranberry growers provided fringe benefits to attract laborers.

provement in the flocks resulted in a wide range of wool quality — ranging from the finest Delaine-Merino to the coarsest carpet. Almost half of the wool clip was profit to the grower.

The cattle industry was important in the territories of Arizona, Utah, Wyoming and Montana. In Idaho, wheat, oats, potatoes and hay were the major crops, and ranchers were working to improve their horses and cattle. Cultivated fields were taking the place of bunchgrass in Washington as they moved away from range farming to providing food and shelter for their stock. The Dakota territory was producing more wheat than any other state or territory in 1888, and was beginning to grow oats, corn, barley and flax. Stock raising was also coming into its own. By 1900, Oklahoma was shipping cotton, flour, wheat, corn and cattle to Europe.

Living conditions for western pioneers varied according to time and place. Foremost was the hard work and drudgery. It wasn't easy to build a productive farm from the raw prairie, the desert or even the forest of the Pacific Northwest. The farmer who was breaking sod on the prairie plains, or clearing land in western Oregon or Washington, or plowing an irrigation ditch in Colorado was engaged in back-breaking effort. Moreover, much of the farm work was dull and monotonous. And even when farm machinery became somewhat cheaper and more efficient in the 1800s, many pioneers did much of their planting, cultivating and harvesting by hand.

**It wasn't easy to build a productive farm from the raw prairie, the desert or even the forest of the Pacific Northwest.**

Housewives of the era faced a life of caring for children, washing, baking, cleaning, sewing, doing outside chores and even working in the fields during busy times. Like the men, the western women worked hard. But frontier people were not prone to self-pity. They only complained if their work failed to produce a decent living.

Frontier farmers suffered their full share of human tragedy from time to time. Poor health, loss of crops and livestock, accidents and untimely death itself plagued all of them. Being far away from relatives and loved ones weighed heavily on families

William Dempster Hoard, the founder of *Hoard's Dairyman*, a national dairy magazine, promoted wise dairying practices. No other name is more intimately identified with the dairy industry of the U.S.

# Cream by Machinery!
# De Laval Cream Separator.
## The Greatest of all Dairy Inventions.

*Extracts the cream from milk fresh from the cow. Saves time. Does away with the need of ice. Leaves the skimmed milk fresh and sweet. Gives 10 to 15 per cent. more and better butter than any other process, and 20 to 25 per cent. more than common setting.*

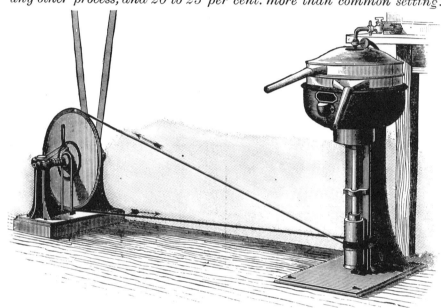

*Never wears out. Soon saves its first cost. Nearly 3,000 in use. Endorsed by the best private butter makers and creameries in the United States and Europe. Simple in construction, it is easily managed and cleaned, and requires less than one-horse power to run.*

*For Catalogue giving full particulars and testimonials of its superiority by hundreds now using it, address*

**Jos. H. Reall, President, 32 Park Row, New York.**

WESTERN OFFICE:—92 Lake St., Chicago.

---

**P. S.**—*The judges of the great English Dairy Fair, just held in London, have made a report of an exhaustive competitive test, resulting in favor of the "DE LAVAL" on every point covered by a Cream Separator. They give it the highest recommendation for superiority in construction, operation and results, that any implement has ever received, and their indorsement clinches the evidence of the great merits and advantages of this most useful of all Dairy appliances. They state that no butter-maker can afford to be without one.*

New inventions made the dairy industry more efficient and profitable.

When farmers and agricultural leaders grew to realize that single cropping was ruining the land many turned to animal husbandry. Dairying, especially, was a favored occupation. These two Jersey cows, Beauty and Jersey, were the property of the Illinois Breeding Association. Breed Associations were established to improve the quality of the stock.

The Babcock butterfat test, developed by Prof. Stephen H. Babcock at the University of Wisconsin in 1890, made it possible to determine the fat content of milk so its quality could be better measured.

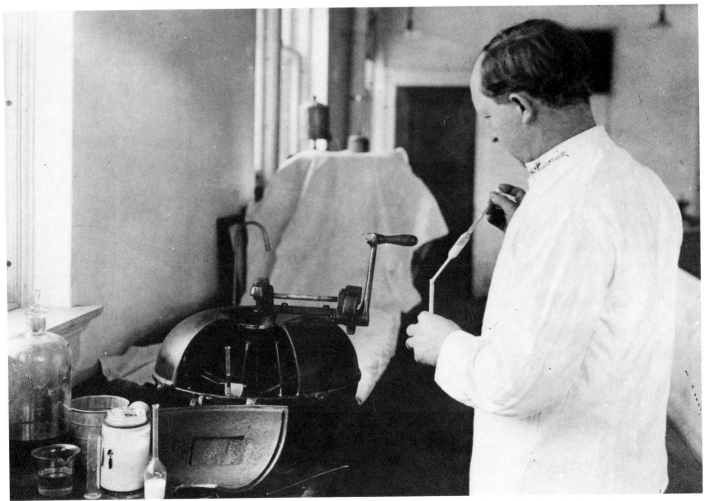

61

Booker T. Washington founded the Tuskegee Institute in 1881. The state of Alabama granted him $2,000 for teachers' salaries. He opened the school in an old church and shanty. His aim was to give the Negro a practical education in industry, trade, and especially agriculture.

trying to make a start in a new country.

But neighbors were never too far away. In most communities there was a great deal of social visiting. Farmers organized and attended singing socials, literary and debate societies, spelling bees, Fourth of July celebrations and Christmas parties. Family gatherings were especially happy occasions.

The isolation of the early western settler prompted him to welcome the occasional visitor with open arms, often offering him a meal and overnight lodging in exchange for the latest news and fellowship.

Pioneering on the last agricultural frontier was marked by a mixture of optimism and bitter disappointment. While many people failed, so many more succeeded. The total number of farms in the United States increased from 2 million in 1860 to 5.7 million in 1900. The improved farm acreage increased from 163 million acres in 1860 to 415 million in 1900.

More land and the growing labor force increased farm production. Agriculture was becoming more mechanized and commercialized. Twine binders were on the market. Spring-tooth harrows were available for seedbed preparation. Horse-drawn combines were used in the Pacific Coast wheat areas. Cream separators were common. Better health and sanitation practices came into effect with the discovery of the tubercle bacillus, the eradication of pleuropneumonia, the determination of the carrier of tick fever and the inspection of dairy products.

By 1900 the newly settled western part of the United States raised almost 50 percent of the country's cattle, 56 percent of the sheep, 25 percent of the hogs, 32 percent of the nation's cereal crops, and 50 percent of the country's wheat. This area represented 17 percent of the total population.

George Washington Carver concluded experimentation at the Tuskegee Institute, in the early 1900s, which led to the discovery of new uses for sweet potatoes, soybeans and peanuts. His contribution to the field of agricultural chemistry expanded the agricultural economy of the South.

# VII
# Gearing Up

## 1901-1920

The era of pioneer farming was almost over. Most of the country's good farmland was privately owned.

The last half of the 19th century was marked by substandard housing and poor living throughout most of the frontier. The roads were in poor condition; wet weather frequently made them impassible. Schools were primitive and facilities for social life inadequate. The clothing and furniture of the time were homemade, very plain and oftentimes uncomfortable.

But the 20th century brought changes to these areas. The forests of the Lake States were cut to provide lumber for homes and barns. Instead of the log cabin or sod house, fairly well constructed frame dwellings were going up. The increase in the supply of lumber also meant that towns were appearing with fairly attractive shopping areas. The roads were graded and kept moderately passable. Bridges were constructed, along with new schools, churches, and lodge halls. Mail-order houses, such as Montgomery Ward and Sears, Roebuck & Co., were supplying more and more of the basic comforts of life. A Rural Free Delivery mail program brought the farmer into touch with more of the world around him. Farm families received more outside news, and kept in a little closer contact with friends and relatives back east.

Now, the farmer was no longer just a self-sufficient producer who grew only what his family could consume. He produced crops or livestock, sold them on the market and then bought the manufactured goods he required. This farmer became more specialized. He concentrated on a few crops or a particular kind of livestock for which his land, location or market was best suited. He felt it was more profitable to devote money and labor to one, or possibly a few commodities, rather than to spread himself too thin.

Regional differences were developing in New Jersey and, to the south, vegetable production came into prominence. Dairy farming became a commercial industry rather than just a sideline in the Lake States and New York. Conditions just weren't suitable to heavy wheat production in these states, but crops such as corn, vegetables and hay thrived. By turning to dairying, farmers could build a more prosperous and permanent agriculture, and allow their soils to rebuild. The rich prairie lands of the West and South were better suited for growing wheat.

Sears, Roebuck & Co., brought the magic of a department store/implement dealer to the nearest post office or mailbox.

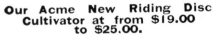

Our Acme New Riding Disc Cultivator at from $19.00 to $25.00.

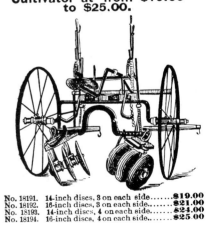

No. 18191.  14-inch discs, 3 on each side.......$19.00
No. 18192.  16-inch discs, 3 on each side.......$21.00
No. 18193.  14-inch discs, 4 on each side.......$24.00
No. 18194.  16-inch discs, 4 on each side.......$25.00

Rural Free Delivery was started in 1893. It began to draw people together. No longer did farmers have to drive many miles to town to get their mail.

A group of farmers met in Texas to found the Farmers Union in 1902. There was an initiation fee of $1 and the dues were 5¢ per month. Its influence grew in Texas and soon spread to Oklahoma. By 1905 there were 200,000 members in 11 southern states.

Southern farmers found it particularly difficult to break away from the mechanical, one-crop farming. However, new varieties of rice had been introduced into southern agriculture and demonstration farms were set up to show that crops other than cotton and tobacco could be grown for profit. The problems of southern agriculture would not be tackled effectively until the 1930s. In the Plains, farmers turned to fencing cattle. The romantic but unstable cattle-range industry was abandoned for more predictable and controllable cattle ranching.

The Far West, especially California, was becoming more of an agricultural area. Improvements in transportation, the growth of irrigation and a marketing system geared to delivering goods to the distant consuming public all contributed to the emergence of a strong agricultural industry.

In the Pacific Northwest the emphasis was still on wheat. The apple and other fruit industries were beginning to respond to forces similar to those in California, but specialized farming still had not taken hold.

The intermountain area was changing the least. Because of natural conditions, fencing just wasn't practical. For this reason, range livestock was still the largest agricultural industry, although more intensive agriculture was beginning to catch on in irrigated areas. Sugar beets thrived in some areas of Colorado and potatoes flourished in Idaho.

As a farmer became more specialized, and more dependent on others, he had to consider economic forces and development outside the world of agriculture. Other industries were changing and growing, too. While the number of farms and people working on farms remained fairly constant, the percentage of the country's population involved in agriculture was decreasing.

This was good news to America's farmers from 1900 to 1914. Farm prices were relatively high compared to prices farmers had to pay. The industrial phases of the economy were growing rapidly enough to absorb increasing production, and the farmer was in a favorable cost/price position. Farm output was expanding at a less rapid pace than industrial output, so there were no large surpluses to depress prices. The rate of acreage being added to production was lower than it had been earlier, and there was an increase in land values. A sound balance had been reached between supply and demand.

The first decade of the new century brought substantial price advances to American farmers. Prices of farm products rose an unprecedented 5 percent between 1900 and 1910.

As the farmer, his animals and crops became more mobile, so did animal and plant diseases. Hoof-and-mouth disease, the boll weevil, grasshoppers, hog cholera, tuberculosis and contagious abortion all were new problems that the growing farm economy had thrust upon its members.

A philosophy was developing among educators that favored working with the farmer to show him good farming techniques. State land-grant colleges found they could work most effectively by establishing county offices. In 1911, the Chamber of Com-

The steam tractor needed an ample fuel and water supply. It packed the soil and was forever setting fires. In spite of its many disadvantages, it was a common sight on some farms by 1900.

This plow was hooked to a steam tractor by a system of cables. This made it possible to plow the field without running the tractor up and down the furrows.

Specialized equipment had been developed for rice threshing.

Some farmers paraded their livestock down Main Street on the way to market.

merce in Broome County, New York, formed a "farm bureau" to carry on educational programs in cooperation with the land-grant college in that area. Agricultural Extension was born.

The Smith-Lever Agricultural Extension Act of 1914 gave this program a nationwide boost. Under this law, the federal government agreed to match state grants for Extension work. Support for this legislation was slow in coming. Even though the agricultural colleges wanted to do more Extension work, they were concerned about the possibility of federal domination in their local programs. Farm representatives in and out of Congress saw this move as an effort to increase production. They believed instead that better markets were needed. Other opponents of the measure thought it was somewhat socialistic, others said it was

The establishment of the agricultural Extension carried ag-education from the university campus to American farms. A county agent advises a farmer in the Kentucky foothills. A Montana home demonstration agent starts for a meeting.

class legislation. Inclusion of the Negro farmers brought about a bitter conflict. The bill was redrafted several times before it was passed.

The Federal-State Extension Service completed a three-cornered program. Teaching had been provided through the Morrill Land-Grant College Act of 1862, research by the Hatch Experiment Stations Act of 1887, and finally the Smith-Lever Agricultural Extension Act of 1914 established the Extension portion of the program.

World War I assured the success of the new Extension service. U.S. policy centered on supplying foodstuffs, producing the ships to carry them, and making loans that would enable nations to continue purchasing from this country. The government quickly extended the county agent network. They were to be the key contacts between governments and farmers in the effort to stimulate food production.

The one act that probably had the most effect on agriculture during the war was the establishment of the Food Administration. This group was to exercise controls over food to bring about conservation, and the effective distribution of available supplies. It was difficult to change the nation's food supply substantially during the United States' brief involvement in the war. The country did realize a moderate increase in production, but there was an enormous increase in demand, resulting in increased prices.

Farmers were pressing for even more specific instruction in agriculture at the secondary and elementary schools. The Smith-Hughes Vocational Education Act of 1917 helped answer this need by providing federal aid to schools, particularly for vocational agricultural education. Support for the act was widespread. Farm organizations pushed "practical" vocational agriculture. President Theodore Roosevelt's Country Life Commission added its influence to the movement when it recommended better agricultural education efforts.

Money was given to states to supplement the subsidies granted

Every neighborhood had a steam tractor and threshing machine which made the rounds in late August. The straw stack was a familiar landmark on farms in the early 20th century.

The victory garden was born during World War I. Farmers and city folks as well turned their efforts to producing extra crops for the war effort. Lou Henry Hoover worked with the Girl Scouts of America to establish victory gardens. The parks of Washington, D.C. were even planted to vegetables.

The Food Administration encouraged farmers to increase production during World War I.

The American farmer fed millions of people in war-ravaged Europe. Herbert Hoover led the efforts which transported food worth billions of dollars to Europe. A supplementary meal was served daily in Belgium schools.

Women calling themselves Farmerettes worked the farms, making it possible for men to undertake war tasks.

to their high schools for introducing agriculture courses. Funds were extended not only for agriculture, but also for trade, industries and home economics.

The Smith-Lever and, to some extent, the Smith-Hughes Act also influenced the formation of 4-H clubs throughout the U.S. In the early 1900s a few Junior Naturalist Clubs, corn clubs and canning clubs had been organized throughout the nation to provide rural young people with a more practical education in farming and homemaking. When the Smith-Lever Act created the national Cooperative Extension Service, a program for boys and girls naturally developed out of the Extension effort.

4-H members select one or more projects, usually in the areas of agriculture, home economics, personal development or community service. They work with an adult leader and receive practical experience in their project areas. The four Hs in the organization's clover emblem are said to "represent the equal training of the head, heart, hands and health of every child." There are currently 4-H clubs in all 50 states.

Another outgrowth of the Smith-Lever Act was the establishment of the American Farm Bureau Federation in 1919. "Farm bureaus" had been set up as local sources of agricultural information, oftentimes at the urging of chambers of commerce. While some bureaus received government financial support, they eventually became more autonomous and were supported by membership dues. In 1917, many local farm bureaus joined together in state federations, and soon formed the American Farm Bureau Federation. AFBF expanded its educational efforts and became active in commercial and political action on behalf of agriculture.

**Cooperatives were originally established to help small farmers gain buying advantages previously available only to large-scale operators.**

One agricultural activity that had its origin in an earlier time but gained a great deal of momentum during this period was the cooperative movement. Cooperatives were originally established to help small farmers gain buying advantages previously available only to large-scale operators. Cooperation enabled individual farm operators to benefit from commercial, credit and operational functions which could not be performed effectively, economically or at all within the limits of family-size farms.

Co-ops probably grew out of the popular barn-raisings, corn huskings and cattle drives of the early 19th century. Cooperative grain elevators were the first practical application of the concept. In the 1850s, cooperative cheese and butter factories were organized in New York and other states. Rural mutual fire insurance companies were started, and some livestock shipping was done on a cooperative basis.

Probably one of the most successful early cooperatives was the California Fruit Growers Exchange, organized in 1895. It became, and still is one of the giants among farmers' cooperatives. It paved the way for farmers to challenge "big business" on its own ground.

College classes in agricultural courses were taken by more and more young men who aspired to become better farmers.

The American Federation of Farmers, later known as the American Farm Bureau Federation, held its first convention in Indianapolis in December, 1920.

Agricultural education became an important part of the high school curriculum.

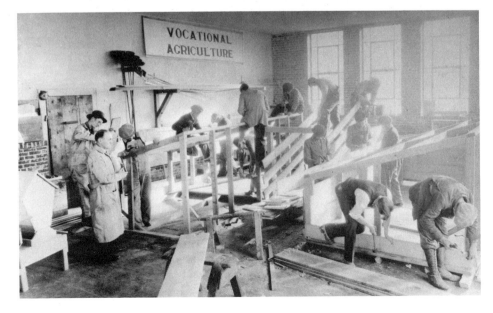

Initially, cooperatives did not have the necessary statutes to organize. There were problems with antitrust laws, but they were resolved in favor of farm cooperatives. State laws were eventually written which made specific provisions for cooperatives.

Most cooperatives were set up along the lines of the Rochdale stores in England. They were run on the basis of one man-one vote, limited return on capital, and the distribution of surplus income in accordance with the amount of business done with the association (patronage refunds).

Cooperatives were originally designed to help meet the needs of the buyer rather than the seller. As they matured, however, sound business practices were stressed, along with service and savings to both the producer and the customer.

The cooperative movement was supported and stimulated by the Grange, Farmers Union, American Society of Equity and American Farm Bureau Federation. By 1920, cooperatives numbered more than 12,000.

There was considerable interest in commodity associations operating over extended areas. Aaron Sapiro, a California attorney, was instrumental in the development of producer marketing co-ops. He became involved in the national movement and advocated that cooperatives handle the entire output of important crops, and get monopoly prices through monopoly control. Sapiro's ideas dominated the cooperative movement for ten years. But the associations could not live up to such high expectations and they never controlled a sufficient portion of any one product to get such an edge on the market.

Post-World War I legislation also helped the cooperative movement. The government authorized the establishment and operation of agricultural cooperatives and provided assistance through the Federal Farm Board of 1929.

**The economic and legislative policies of both government and farmer organizations had an important effect on this period of agricultural history.**

The economic and legislative policies of both government and farmer organizations had an important effect on this period of agricultural history. But the real catalyst was the development of the internal combustion engine.

Actually, mechanized farm equipment development began during the 1800s. Consider the steam traction engine. It was designed especially for threshing machines and was first manufactured in 1849. By 1900 more than 30 firms were manufacturing a total of 5,000 large steam traction engines every year.

The steam engines presented problems to everyone except the very largest farm operators. They were so heavy that a farmer couldn't plow or do any other work without packing the soil. Sparks from the smokestacks frequently started fires. Something better was needed.

The internal combustion engine had been invented and improved in Europe during the late 1800s. By 1890 American firms began marketing the stationary engine. Their next step was to mount it on wheels, make it portable, and incorporate a drive that made it self-propelled. The tractor had been invented!

John Froelich of Froelich, Iowa, built the first successful gasoline tractor in 1892. He put the tractor to test by taking it on a 50-day threshing run. He ran the tractor over rough ground and operated it in temperatures ranging from -3 to 100 degrees Fahrenheit. Froelich's tractor amounted to an Ohio-made gasoline engine mounted on a running gear fitted with a transmission he built himself.

The Hart-Parr Company, Charles City, Iowa, was the first business in the United States devoted exclusively to manufacturing

The Wallis tractor by J.I. Case was one of the early "modern" tractors.

Henry Ford introduced the Fordson in 1917 as the world's first mass-produced tractor. Ford said that the farm and the farmer were "close to his heart" and he conducted experiments on agricultural mechanization on his 9,000-acre farm.

tractors. C.W. Hart and C.H. Parr studied and built gasoline engines while they were students at the University of Wisconsin in 1895. After graduating, they set up a business manufacturing a line of small stationary engines and developed a system of cooling the cylinders with oil. Water had been used previously and the problems farmers had with evaporation and freezing are easy to imagine. But oil cooling made their engine particularly well-suited to farming.

As enterprising farm boys, Hart and Parr quickly realized the potential market for gasoline traction engines, which they called the "tractor". In 1902, they sold their first one. It operated successfully for 20 years. The second year, they built and sold 15 tractors, developed a plowing tractor and perfected and adapted their oil cooling system to the tractor. A little later, Hart and Parr fitted their engines with a device enabling the tractor to burn less expensive kerosene and fuel oil distillate.

Demand for the Hart-Parr tractor quickly exceeded supply. The tractor was long overdue, in the minds of most farmers. Hart-Parr facilities expanded until the plant covered an area one mile in length by one-half mile in width and by 1917, Hart-Parr had over 1,000 people on the payroll.

Hart-Parr Number 1 built in 1901 and the Hart-Parr Company at Charles City, Iowa.

The Little Devil.

Hart-Parr made a tractor called "Little Devil". It had a 2-cycle engine, strong, simple construction and could burn cheap fuel. When the Little Devil was first marketed in 1914, the Charles City Press wrote:

"The adage that 'if you build something that the world wants, the world will beat a pathway to your door' was surprisingly manifested. Orders began to flood in before circulars had been prepared. The Hart-Parr Company was not surprised . . . It is every inch a quality tractor, frame, wheels, power plant — everything — has all the elements of thoroughly dependable design, highest grade material and finest workmanship. The Little Devil has the stored energy of seven horses. It will do everything a horse will do. It will plow corn and all the subsequent duties of civilization; it will plow, drag, roll and seed the small grain; then harvest, husk, shred, fill the silo, shell corn and every farm duty in growing large and small grains. For a little more than the price of a good stationary engine, it will do all the belt work. It will run the separator, hitch up the light plant, pump water and make chores a memory of the past. A farmer can sell his horses, buy a Little Devil and put the balance in the bank. When he does that, he puts his farm on an efficiency basis. He will raise more and easier. He will put dollars of added value in every acre."

The Little Devil was said to be "thoroughly competent, trim as a Kentucky Thoroughbred, and husky as a Jim Jeffries in his prime."

The heaviest expansion of farm machinery manufacture came from 1915 to 1920, and then again after 1940 when the country had become the leading capitalist nation. But it wasn't until 1950 that there were more tractors than horses on American farms.

# VIII
# Dark Days

## 1921-1932

The "Agricultural Revolution" started with the 20th century. A lot was happening — fast!

Enclosed gears were developed for the tractor, and a successful light tractor had been perfected. Multiple-row cultivators, corn planters and corn pickers came into wide use. And many farmers had adopted an all-purpose rubber-tired tractor with complementary equipment.

**A lot was happening — fast!**

The number of man-hours required to produce one acre of wheat and one acre of corn was reduced by more than half. In the late 1800s it took 8 to 10 man-hours to produce one acre, or 20 bushels, of wheat; and 14 to 16 man-hours to produce one acre, or 40 bushels, of corn. But by the 1920s only 3 to 4 man-hours were needed to produce one acre of wheat, and 6 to 8 man-hours for one acre of corn.

Technical improvements in farm operations were also given a boost by the widespread use of electrical power.

Commercial fertilizers, fungicides, weed killers and insecticides were being used more and more. Agricultural scientists had discovered that certain chemicals could change the growth of plants, just like hormones control the growth and development of animals. Chemicals like 2, 4-D received farmers' attention.

Better understanding of genetics led to plant hybridization and improved varieties. Early work by George Mendel, who established the basic laws of inheritance of specific characteristics, and Charles Darwin, who worked with inbreeding, was put to practical use. William James Beal, a botany professor at the Michigan Agricultural College during the 1880s, crossed two varieties of corn by detasseling one which then received pollen only from the other variety that was planted in adjacent rows.

In the early 1900s scientists showed that corn loses its vigor through successive generations of self-pollination, or inbreeding. They also learned that increased vigor and bigger yields could be regained by crossing the inbred lines.

At the Connecticut experimental station, Donald F. Jones developed a practical means of producing hybrid corn.

By 1925 several experiment stations and private plant breeders were getting excellent hybrid results. In 1926 Henry A. Wallace, who was later to become Secretary of Agriculture, established

The general store at the crossroads carried everything from bloomers to cod-liver oil. It was still the favorite meeting place for farmers and ranchers and a heated political discussion could get a little loud.

As farm families became established on their homesteads, the frame home housed successive generations.

the first seed company for the commercial production of hybrid corn. This development has been called one of the greatest accomplishments of modern times. A University of Chicago researcher estimated that the annual return on expenditures for research of hybrid corn was in the neighborhood of 700 percent!

Numbers of farms decreased, while farm size increased. There was also a gradual leveling off, then a decline in the number of acres under cultivation. At the same time, however, the production of crops and livestock was increasing dramatically. And while the commercial farmer's standard of living was better than at any time in American history, his per capita income was only about half that of urban dwellers.

The nation was in a transition. People became more interested in what was going on in the city than what was happening down on the farm. Rural adjustment problems were delayed and intensified by the relative prosperity farmers enjoyed during World War I.

It was almost impossible during the war to make any improvements in the farmstead. Farmers saved money in the form of Liberty Bonds, but many did not hold them for the future. The high earnings of farmland generated a major land boom. Farmland and building valuation almost doubled between 1910 and 1920. The amount farmers owed on real estate mortgages more than doubled in the same period. So after some unprecedented prosperity, farmers were poorer, their land and buildings were more run-down, and their debts larger than they had been before the war began.

Why? Because farmers had never really had any experience with inflation. They were prepared for a depression when the war ended; but when demand picked up and prices moved higher, they believed that a new, permanent and higher level of prices had been established.

The limited period of prosperity following World War I was probably caused by the European nations' desperate need for continuing outside help. They couldn't buy through normal channels, but the United States did permit them to use some of the unextended credit left over from the war.

The beginning of financial difficulties for the farmers came when the U.S. government realized it was becoming the world's greatest creditor nation. If the nation were to continue exporting at the prewar rate, it had to take in more imports or extend more loans. It didn't want to do either. So when it discontinued wartime credits to the allied countries in June of 1919, there was a sudden and catastrophic drop in foreign demand for American agricultural products. This reduction in demand did not mean reduced exports, but lower prices paid for the exports. Once agricultural products had been produced, they had to move. The price paid for them was determined by the amount the foreign countries were willing to pay. As a result, wheat prices dropped to less than half, corn to a third and hogs to less than a half of what they had been. Wool became almost unsaleable. Another problem was the railroads' rate increase. It coincided with the beginning of the price decline on farm products in the fall of 1920 and in early 1921.

The "Caterpillar" Sixty with a Model 30 "Holt" Harvestor was among the multi-row pieces of machinery used extensively in the West.

One of the earliest cotton pickers was given a field test on a southern farm.

The development of pesticides encouraged fruit growers to spray for insects.

By spring, 1921, American agriculture had reached the worst position it had been in at any time since the nation's beginning. According to Congressional reports, the purchasing power of farm products in terms of nonagricultural products was down to 63 percent from prewar levels.

Many farmers had large debts because they had purchased land during the speculative boom of the two preceding years. Rural banks held many farmers' notes that could not be quickly liquidated. The Federal Reserve Board's tight money policy only added to the difficulties of financing agricultural operations.

Farmers and stockmen received daily market reports on livestock and grain in a "listening room", that was often established by local banks.

The privy, outhouse, two-holer — call it what you will — was now being replaced on the farmstead with indoor facilities. To the Halloween pranksters this meant the beginning of the end of the late-night tipover.

The situation became so severe that farmers in the Dakotas and Nebraska were burning corn for fuel, and trading wood for needed socks and shirts.

The farmers of the period faced more than a loss of profits. The prices they received had fallen far below their cost of production. They knew that price-making influences were beyond their individual control, so they undertook a variety of self-help programs. Steeped in a tradition of self-reliance, they believed that they could be helped through application of rigorous economies.

Farmers simply spent less. The farm families scaled down their standard of living. This meant interruption of education, lower levels of health, less recreation and returning to the days of home slaughtering, canning, dressmaking, and baking. Hired farm labor was pared down, and the women and children in many families went to work in the fields. Obsolete farm machinery was not replaced, and worn-out equipment was wired together to "make do". Farmers turned to ag Extension for better farm management techniques. They used disease-resistant seeds adapted to their soil and climate. They applied fertilizers in tested quantities, adopted insect and disease controls, modified rotation schedules, used their machinery more carefully and kept careful farm records.

Many migrated out of agriculture. Government reports show that the farm population dropped by 478,000 in 1922 and by 234,000 in 1923. Farmers turned to other jobs.

Some tried to diversify their operations because they believed several sources of income made for less risk. This was difficult for those farms whose credit, equipment and farm organization were geared to specialization, and where the geography allowed little flexibility.

Voluntary crop reduction schemes were promoted, but this movement lacked direction and incentive. As an individual, a farmer could never gain by producing less. The cooperative movement gained momentum to bypass the middlemen and speculators. While agricultural cooperatives helped the farmers, they left a lot of the problems unsolved.

Farmers soon came to realize that they couldn't be as effective as they had to be without garnering the support and assistance of government on a large scale. It was time to organize and get involved. The newly formed American Farm Bureau Federation began an extensive campaign for farm legislation, as did the Grange and Farmers Union.

Early in 1921, J.G. Brown of the Indiana Farm Bureau wrote Secretary of Agriculture Henry C. Wallace: "The farmers must have a voice in settling important issues. If we fail at this time to have agriculture recognized as it should be, we will not overcome it in the next quarter of a century . . . I have advised Mr. Howard (president of the American Farm Bureau Federation) to call an Executive Committee meeting . . . so we can go over the situation with you and be ready with a well-thought-out program before members of Congress get their minds made up."

The efforts of farm leaders, both in and out of Congress, resulted in the establishment of a farm bloc in both houses of Congress. The group was comprised of members from both political parties with representation from all geographic areas. The bloc had large voting strength and was not accountable to the usual types of party discipline.

In 1921, the bloc passed several measures that were of interest to farmers. One act subjected stockyards to regulation of rates and practices as public service corporations. The bill was designed to eliminate monopoly practices. Another act placed a tax on all sales of grain for future delivery. It was designed to eliminate speculation on the boards of trade, but was invalidated by the Supreme Court less than a year later.

Twelve Production Credit Corporations were established in 1921 to work with commercial banks in developing policies for short- and intermediate-term credit to farmers for production purposes.

Sorghum and molasses were the end products of grinding cane.

Canning and preserving food meant a full larder for winter eating.

The farm bloc was also successful in passing the Capper-Volstead Act of 1922. This law provided that individual agricultural producers who act together through a cooperative association, thereby eliminating competition among themselves, would not be in violation of the antitrust statutes. Capper-Volstead freed cooperatives from the threat of federal prosecution for restraining trade.

Legislators and farm leaders were in a traditional rut during the early 1920s. Most of the programs they wanted were the kinds that had been advocated in the past. Farm production was still high, and foreign markets were uncertain and depressed. The enacted legislation was not having a great effect, and some leaders began to talk about more radical measures.

"You can't sell a plow to a busted customer," said George Peek, of the Moline Plow Company. So Peek and his associate, Hugh Johnson, came up with a proposal that they said would provide "Equality for Agriculture".

Their plan, known as the McNary-Haugen Bill, passed Congress twice but was vetoed both times by President Calvin Coolidge. The plan provided that the federal government set up an export corporation to dispose of surplus crops. Working independently or with private agencies, this corporation would purchase surplus quantities of major commodities above domestic requirements. They would then sell these commodities abroad at world prices. The losses on foreign sales as well as the operating costs would be paid by the farmers through an equalization fee, or tax, on each bushel or pound of a commodity sold. This program was designed to allow farmers to receive their "fair exchange value", later called parity, for their products.

At the fair exchange value, the prices received by farmers would be as high, relative to the prices of those items farmers had to purchase, as they were during 1906 to 1915.

As first introduced, the bill applied to wheat, corn, cotton, wool, cattle, sheep, swine and rice. It was modified as it went through the legislative process to meet specific objections and gain support. But it never did please President Coolidge. He believed the bill was not framed to aid the farmers as a whole, but calculated to hurt them. Coolidge was concerned that the bill placed a premium on one-crop farming, and ignored the recommendations of science. It also ignored farmers engaged in farming so-called "safe" crops such as dairy, beef, sheep, poultry, potatoes, hay, fruit, vegetables, oats, barley, flax, etc. The President said he did not want to put the government in the business of price fixing. He also believed the act would be impossible to administer. Finally, he didn't want to put a direct tax on "certain of vital necessaries of life". He said the equalization fee was not a true tax, but an unconstitutional delegation of the taxing power of Congress. He said it was "the most vicious form of taxation".

McNary-Haugen became an important political issue during the campaign of 1928. Secretary of Commerce, and then presidential candidate, Herbert Hoover opposed the act. His election marked the end of one of the most sustained and bitter struggles over a specific piece of agricultural legislation in the nation's history.

But it did not mark the end of legislative debate on the subject. Price stabilization through subsidized surplus disposal would continue to be an important issue.

The boll weevil was no more "just a looking for a home". It had found one in the southern cotton fields where it caused millions of dollars of damage during the 1920s and 30s.

A harvesting crew took time out for a favorite all-American treat — the watermelon.

Hoover's answer to the McNary-Haugen Act was the Agricultural Marketing Act of 1929. This proposal went further in the direction of government participation in agricultural affairs than the administration wanted, but not quite as far as the farm organizations would have liked. The legislation established a Federal Farm Board to administer a revolving fund of $500 million to be loaned to co-ops for more effective marketing.

When long-term depression extended to the rest of the economy, the task of the Farm Board became impossible. Its final report stated that business recovery was essential to the restoration of farm income. The board also stressed that effective control of production was essential.

The problems of agriculture weighed heavily on young and old alike. Young people on America's farms wanted to learn better farming methods so they could help improve agriculture's plight. In 1928 the Future Farmers of America was founded "to strengthen instruction for students in vocational agriculture by providing a laboratory for practical training in agriculture, leadership, cooperation and citizenship". The FFA incorporated by an act of Congress (Public Law 740), provided the necessary framework.

Thirty-three official delegates representing 18 states attended the organizational meeting of the FFA in 1928 in Kansas City, Missouri. By 1950, 50 state associations (including the Commonwealth of Puerto Rico) were affiliated with the FFA. Alaska is the only state that does not, as yet, have a state association.

It began as and still is, an integral part of vocational-agriculture education in the public school system. FFA activities encourage members to learn through active participation how to conduct and take part in public meetings, to speak in public, to buy and sell cooperatively, to solve their own problems, to finance themselves and to assume civic responsibility.

The goal of a national organization of vocational agriculture students became a reality with the establishment of the FFA in 1928.

# IX

# From the Dust

## 1933-1940

When farmers in the Southern Plains planted their seed in 1933, they were concerned that the soil was drier than it had ever been. The winter passed with very little snow. Wheat was thin and stunted, the topsoil was powder. The country had been dry for almost a year and a half. When strong winds whipped up some dust in February and March, Plains farmers were concerned that this was not an ordinary drought. On April 14, 1934, they were convinced of it.

**The sun bore down, and the wind kept blowing.**

On that day, every field in Kansas came apart. Incredible air currents rushing down from the north sucked up the topsoil and sent it rolling along in a fine cloud. For a while the dust hugged the surface. As the storm increased, the dust rose higher and higher. Visibility shrank from miles to yards. By noon the wind was picking up great chunks of earth and a huge gray cloud of dust was rolling from Kansas southward towards Texas. The cloud extended west to east in a straight line from horizon to horizon. Towns along its path were engulfed before people could get inside and shut their doors.

As the cloud approached, there was a great rush of wind. Then darkness came over the area. The darkness was dust. Windows turned black; dust sifted into the houses through the cracks around the doors and windows; sparks flew between pieces of metal and people got shocks if they touched the plumbing. Food on dinner tables was ruined; milk turned black; beds, furniture, rugs, clothes in the closet, even food in the refrigerators — all were covered with a film of dust. Darkness held on for about three hours after the blackest part of the storm had passed.

Though March and April had been windy and dry, it would rain in May. Farmers hoped and prayed that a rainfall would not fail them two years in a row.

But it did not rain in May, 1934. The sun bore down, and the wind kept blowing. Temperatures reached more than 100 degrees in the shade.

Until the morning of May 10th, the dust storms had been more or less local, covering a few counties at a time. But then the whole countryside seemed to stir at once. A light brown ball of dust rose from 1,000 to 15,000 feet and obscured the sun from the Texas Plains all the way north through the Dakotas. The storm was like nothing the country had ever known.

A sifting dust storm surrounded Guymon, Oklahoma, on April 6, 1935.

*Top facing page:* The winds blew through Dodge City, Kansas, at 10 a.m., March 30, 1935.

*Bottom facing page:* Dust covered the roads . . .

. . . travel came to a standstill.

A small boy was lost on his way home from school near Hays, Kansas. Two hundred people searched a day and a half and finally found him nearly covered with sand less than a quarter of a mile from home. A farmer became lost in his 10-acre garden and roamed around for eight hours, choking and blinded by the dust, before he stumbled against his home.

The wind was from the west this time, and it pushed a wall of dust eastward at 60 to 100 miles an hour. Chicago and the Ohio Valley were surrounded with dust by nightfall. Airplane service between Chicago and St. Paul was delayed. Associated Press reports out of Chicago said that "the entire area from Montana on the west, Texas on the south, and the Ohio Valley in the east" was dusted in.

By the 12th of May, a film of dust hovered over the Eastern Seaboard. It shut out the sun for five hours in New York, Baltimore and Washington D.C.

**Dust sifted in through the windows at the White House and covered President Roosevelt's desk.**

Dust sifted in through the windows at the White House and covered President Roosevelt's desk.

By the 13th of May, ships that were 300 miles out in the Atlantic Ocean reported that dust was settling on the decks, and they radioed shore stations for an explanation.

Whole fields had been swept bare. Millions of acres of crops had been destroyed.

While occasional storms had adverse effects on much of the country, the area known as the Dust Bowl was hardest hit for the next few years. The Dust Bowl included eastern Colorado and New Mexico, the northwest portion of Texas, the Oklahoma Panhandle, and the western part of Kansas. It seemed as if dust was always in the air.

The Southern Plains had experienced prolonged droughts before, but never with such serious and disastrous effects. It was different now because the soil was exhausted from continuous planting of the same crop — wheat, corn or cotton. The roots of the cultivated crops did not form the underground net that the closely woven buffalo grass had provided. The humus was gone; the topsoil was loose and ready to blow. Much of this land had been in cultivation for only 10 or 15 years; but it would take generations to rebuild.

A group of concerned farmers and businessmen gathered at Guymon, Oklahoma, in June, 1934, and issued the following report:

"Cattle were dying on the ranches. Sixty cattle died that very day between Guymon and Liberal, Kansas, of some disease induced by the dust . . .Around Perryton, Texas, an area which for years had yielded four to six million bushels, only a few bushels of wheat were left. Despite the huge surplus that had piled up on the farms in 1931, there was not more than half enough grain in all the thirty counties represented at Guymon to plant another wheat crop . . . Ninety percent of the poultry

Dust drifted around the farm machinery.

Drifts almost covered a farmstead at Dodge City, Kansas.

Refugees fled the Dust Bowl area with all their worldly goods and sought work further west. Some found jobs as migratory farm laborers in California.

were dead in one Texas Panhandle county because of sandstorms . . . Milk cows going dry, turned into the highways to starve . . . Hogs were so lean that buyers would not take them at any price . . . Human beings were suffering from dust fever . . . More than a third of the population in many counties already were dependent upon charity or relief . . . Ninety percent of the farmers in some counties had applied for emergency crop loans; now they were having to use the money for medicine and food, or starve."

Many farm families moved away. They traveled east or westward to the orchards and vegetable fields of California, or the timberlands in the Pacific Northwest.

While the Dust Bowl area was plagued with serious drought, the farmers in the rest of the country were unhappy, too. The Depression had hit them hard, and they were anxious to improve the situation. Some farmers resorted to violent action in order to get what they referred to as "cost of production" prices.

Crop withholding was tried by the Society of Equity, the Farmers Union and commodity organizations in the South. Probably the most colorful of those who turned to violent means to demonstrate their point was Milo Reno of Wapello, Iowa.

Reno was an ordained minister, and former president of the Iowa Farmers Union. He urged farmers to refuse to deliver farm products to market at prices which were lower than production costs. He helped organize the Farmers' Holiday Association in Des Moines, Iowa, in May, 1932. The so-called holiday started in August. Farmers engaged in picketing, constructed barricades and forced dumping of produce.

President Franklin D. Roosevelt signed the Agricultural Adjustment Act into law.

The situation was frequently too much for the local sheriff to handle and the governor of Iowa imposed martial law in some areas. The farmers used threat and force to stop mortgage sales. In one courtroom, they dragged the judge from the bench, threatened him with lynching and choked him momentarily — all because he refused to promise he would never sign a foreclosure paper.

Farmers won temporary victories as a result of this type of action, but realized few real gains. They did, however, point up the seriousness of the situation.

The federal government was beginning to realize it had to come up with programs that would help bring the country, and especially agriculture, out of the depressed economic state. Steps had to be taken to assist all of the farmers, whether they were plagued by drought, depleted soil, serious credit problems, low prices, or high expenses.

Franklin D. Roosevelt became President in 1933, and initiated programs the likes of which the country had never seen. It was all a part of the New Deal.

One of the first pieces of legislation enacted under the New Deal was the Farm Credit Act of 1933. This cleared away the obsolete and unworkable phases of earlier credit legislation. For the first time in the country's history, a balanced, practical and

Millions of acres of Tennessee Valley land were so badly eroded in the early 1930s that crop production was impossible.

The Tennessee Valley Authority (TVA) rescued farmland in the seven-state region. They cooperated with the Extension in teaching farmers how to halt the loss of soil into the Tennessee and its tributaries through terracing and other conservation methods.

Tennessee Valley farms responded well to TVA fertilizer and modern management practices.

TVA's total rehabilitation program provided electric power to area farms. At the same time, the REA was taking electricity to many parts of rural America.

comprehensive system of federally sponsored agricultural credit agencies was provided. The bill set up the Farm Credit System — 12 regional land banks for making mortgage loans, 13 banks for making loans to cooperatives, and 12 production credit corporations to provide short-term and intermediate-term credit. Federal Land Bank Associations and Production Credit Associations were established to reach and serve individual farmers and ranchers. While the act was designed to meet credit emergencies, it became a major source of agricultural credit in normal times. The highly successful Farm Credit System is now entirely farmer-rancher owned.

The Roosevelt administration wanted to systematically adjust farm production to meet market demands. The Agricultural Adjustment Act of 1933 was designed to do just that.

The Agricultural Adjustment Administration (AAA) was given broad authority: it could contract with farmers to adjust production; make government loans on crops; distribute surplus food to the needy; and levy a processing tax as a means of financing the crop reduction program.

Between 1933 and 1935, benefit payments were sent to farmers who voluntarily contracted (and complied) with the government to reduce production. Farmers' cash receipts and net incomes increased slightly. Crop inventories were reduced. While recovery in the nonfarm sector and heavy expenditures for relief deserve most of the credit for improving the situation, the AAA will long be remembered for its immediate impact on agriculture.

The Supreme Court invalidated the production control provisions of the act in early January, 1936. Congress quickly responded by passing the Soil Conservation and Domestic Allotment Act the very next month. The act was designed to reduce surplus crop production through payments for improved land use and conservation practices. Direct payments were made to farmers for complying with acreage and marketing restrictions on certain "soil depleting" crops. A constant theme was to encourage farmers to carry out specified soil-conserving measures.

Along with establishing the Soil Conservation Service (SCS), the act was intended to help Dust Bowl farmers redirect agriculture from intensive to more extensive types of farming, and forego volume in the short run in the interest of restoring and maintaining the productivity of the soil.

The New Deal also produced the Rural Electrification Administration (REA) in 1935. Secretary of Agriculture Wallace said this move would have "an influence on farm life somewhat comparable to that which has been brought to pass by the automobile and the hard roads".

The REA was set up to establish terms and standards to increase the availability of electric power in rural areas much like the Tennessee Valley Authority. Rural electric cooperatives were formed and applied for loans to build lines. Electricity used on

Henry A. Wallace was FDR's Secretary of Agriculture. An Iowan, he was the son of Henry C. Wallace, who served in the same position between 1921 and 1924. Henry A. went on to be vice-president under Roosevelt between 1941 and 1945.

farms increased substantially. In 1929, only 580,000 farms had electric service; by 1933, 774,000; and by 1937, 1.2 million. This figure doubled by 1941.

The Agricultural Adjustment Act of 1933 and the Soil Conservation and Domestic Allotment Act of 1936 were looked upon as temporary measures. They needed further refinement. So the Agricultural Adjustment Act of 1938 was born. It added special provisions for water conservation and erosion control in arid and semiarid range areas, in addition to soil conservation. It authorized the Secretary of Agriculture to intervene on behalf of agriculture in cases before the Interstate Commerce Commission with respect to freight rates. It also dealt with agricultural loans, parity payments, consumer safeguards, marketing quotas and it created the Federal Crop Insurance Corporation.

All this elaborate government machinery for adjusting farm production to demand was only partially successful. Agricultural efficiency and productivity was increasing to the point that it was difficult to assure farmers a "fair price". Even though total

During the Great Depression farmers had to make do with what they had. This farmer was lucky enough to find enough gas to transport his last pig to market.

The Civilian Conservation Corps was established to provide jobs for young men. The CCC boys worked on reforesting, terracing, and other conservation projects that helped maintain and save the soil. The Roosevelt Administration created many organizations which were and still are recognized by their initials.

acreage harvested was 38 million less in 1939 than in 1929, total agricultural production was higher. Net farm income rose from $1.9 billion in 1932 to $4.2 billion in 1940, but prices were not close to parity and the government held large surpluses of agricultural products in storage.

Nevertheless, the New Deal programs had moved agriculture away from some grave economic problems and into somewhat better times. The U.S. was moving into the role of world food and fiber provider.

The farm auction provided bargains galore.

Three or four good horses could pull the binder. If the bundles were kept in straight rows it made for easier shocking.

Not pickin' peas — but cutting peas for the local cannery. Cannery crops produced on a large scale became an important part of agriculture.

# X
# At Full Capacity

## 1941-1949

**"Food will win the war and write the peace."**

The attack on Pearl Harbor, December 7, 1941, drawing the United States into a second world war, inspired a new sense of unity in the nation. Everyone, including farmers, rallied to aid the country and her allies in this effort.

The emphasis suddenly switched from grave concern over low prices and ways to reduce production to better prices and pleas for increased production. USDA appealed to farmers' patriotism with the slogan, "Food will win the war and write the peace." The New Deal emergency programs were replaced by tremendous demands for food and fiber.

Crop controls and other restrictions were eased. Farmers were paid incentives to speed up production, instead of getting paid for keeping land idle. Sharp farm-product price increases were allowed. Over 400 million bushels of wheat and enormous quantities of corn were released from storage.

The soil conservation techniques inspired by New Deal programs helped assure adequate wartime production. Farmers had begun to conserve their soil and obtain higher yields by strip-, contour- and terrace-farming.

America was to become the breadbasket of the world. She had the responsibility to feed her allies, as well as to arm them.

Much of the increased farm production can be attributed to the greater use of lime and commercial fertilizer. Direct government supervision of the fertilizer industry kept it operating at full capacity during the war years. As a result, fertilizer use increased from 8.3 million tons in 1939-40 to 12.5 million in 1944. Fertilizer was available for more acres of victory gardens, commercial vegetables, truck crops and potatoes. Lime and phosphate were put on hay and pastureland, which promoted good crop rotation programs. Green manuring — plowing under crops like clover and ryegrass — became a popular way of adding to soil fertility.

The war economy stimulated the conversion from animal to mechanical power on the farm. The gradual shift to tractors and other complementary equipment brought an increased output per worker. Farmers could do the job faster and better, and realize greater benefits.

However, there was a shortage of raw materials for farm equipment because much of the country's steel was directed to

Put your muscle on a war basis!

SIGN UP FOR A FARM JOB
...at your local U.S. Employment Office

Schools closed early in the year and everybody was urged to get involved in farm work. City cousins were encouraged to seek employment on the farms instead of working for higher wages in the city.

Strip farming, contour tillage and terracing farmland were conservation practices that came into wide use to save the soil.

the production of munitions and war-related goods. The farm industry was alarmed when in 1943 the War Production Board proposed allocating only 23 percent as much steel for farm machinery production as was used in 1940. USDA protested and managed to raise the allocation to 40 percent, but the industry had a difficult time obtaining even as much steel as had been allocated. So the sale of farm machinery was rationed to dealers on the basis of area needs in meeting national food production goals.

In those areas hardest hit by shortages, farmers pooled their equipment with neighbors. Sharing tractors, combines and other machines meant fewer slowdowns in crop cultivation and harvesting. Custom or contract operators came as a result of this pooling.

In spite of some severe shortages, farmers did manage to get more equipment during the war years, notably tractors, sprayers and harvesting and haying machinery. A few inventions were introduced, including the one-man hay baler, the cotton picker, a hydraulic system for tractors, Ferguson's 3-point hitch and complementary equipment.

The switch from animal to mechanical power had another positive effect on farming that nobody anticipated. The decrease in "animal power" — some 15 million horses and mules from 1920 to 1946 — released land to grow feed for an equivalent number of productive livestock. The saving in grain alone in 1946 amounted to 16 million tons — enough to feed 32 million hogs to market weight. More available feed meant more feed per animal, more livestock fed and more meat, dairy and poultry production. Feed quality improved. Rations were more balanced. The protein content of hay increased. Animals were fed

*Facing page:* Windmill power was becoming obsolete on many farms. Some powered their pumps with electricity.

During World War II farmers blew the dust off the old churns and took to making their own butter again.

The "farm work force" made do with a large victory garden and a lot of hard work. They had to save the precious ration coupons for the barest necessities of food. They still wore a smile to hasten the end of the War. Much of the old machinery around the farm went to the scrap drive to be made into tanks and ammunition. Paper and foil were given to the War effort. Tojo, Hitler, Iwo Jima, Normandy and Rommel became household words. Everybody tuned in the radio to H.V. Kaltenborn or Gabriel Heatter to hear the latest word from the Front. Amost every farmhouse had a star in the window . . . and some had gold ones.

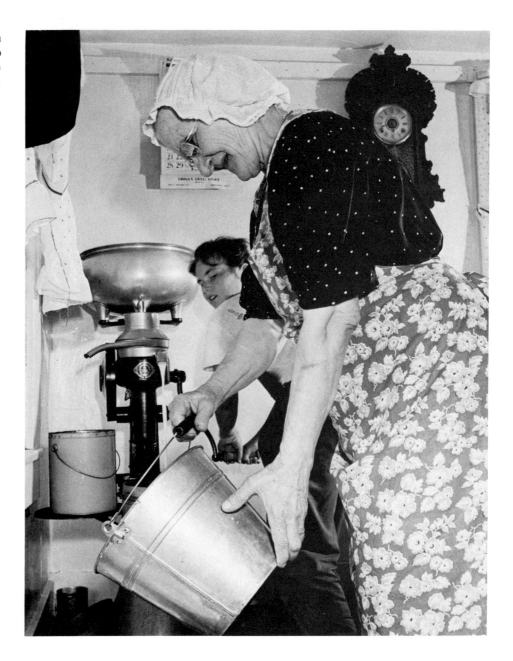

With Johnny off to War, Grandma
and the children were drafted into
the ranks of farm workers to
separate the cream.

high-protein oil-seed meal along with their corn.

The adoption of hybrid seed corn meant more bushels per acre. About 78 percent of the corn produced in the Corn Belt in 1943 was from hybrid seed.

Skilled farm workers were scarce. The military draft, enlistments and the attraction of high wages in the war industries drained the farm labor supply. Farm workers migrated out of farming when the war hit. Farm wage rates and working conditions were at a competitive disadvantage when compared to wartime employment opportunities. By early 1943, commercial agriculture was worried that it would not have enough help to plant and harvest that year's crop.

The government stepped in and granted "essential farm worker" draft deferments to almost two million men. They comprised 12 to 15 percent of the people working on farms; but because they were young and able-bodied, they contributed a far higher percentage of total work output.

American GIs fed Italian children during World War II. Heavy demands were made on U.S. agriculture during and after the War to feed millions caught in the conflict.

President Harry Truman initiated the Marshall Plan for the rehabilitation of those countries that had been devastated during the War. The American farmer again provided millions of tons of food for the refugees of Europe and Asia.

The armed forces had been given priority on food. Vegetable, grain and livestock producers doubled their efforts, but there were still some shortages. Eggs, meat, butter and some vegetables were scarce commodities for many civilians. Food rationing was implemented to prevent hoarding and to insure a more equal distribution of scarce items.

Through the war effort, U.S. food and fiber production reached an all-time high. The country's output exceeded that of any country in the world. The combination of high prices and heavy production caused net farm income to jump about 100 percent from $6.6 billion in 1941 to $12.4 billion in 1945. Farmers were able to pay off debts, buy savings bonds and improve their living standards.

This was the first prosperity most of them had known for over 20 years.

As World War II ended, American agriculture was a substantial industry operating at full capacity. The postwar success can be traced to the government's rebuilding program for the European nations. Through the Marshall Plan, the U.S. supplied European countries with goods they were not able to provide for themselves. It received widespread support in the United States and helped the war-torn countries rebuild their economies at an amazing rate.

**Through the war effort, U.S. food and fiber production reached an all-time high.**

In 1947, agricultural prices reached 115 percent of parity and net farm income climbed to $15.5 billion.

Remembering the developments of 20 years earlier, farmers had taken prior steps to protect themselves against a postwar depression. They convinced Congress to guarantee them prices at 90 percent of parity on a select list of commodities for two years after the war. It was the Stabilization Act of 1942.

But this authorization for high-level price support was running out in 1948, and Congress took a new look at farm programs. The Agricultural Act of 1948, among other things, developed a new parity formula and a flexible price support feature. Though extremely complicated, it was an attempt to reflect changes in the demand and cost situation which had occurred since the 1910-14 base period, and yet retain the 1910-14 relationship as an overall criterion of equity between farm and nonfarm prices.

Farm leaders and congressmen were quite fond of the parity concept, however, and didn't want to abandon it for something they thought would be vague and subject to Executive decision. So, they updated the old policy, instead of developing a more relevant one.

The new price support feature provided an absolute floor of 50 percent and an absolute maximum of 90 percent support on "basic" crops — corn, cotton, wheat, rice, tobacco and peanuts. In time of serious national need, a higher ceiling could be authorized. For "nonbasic" crops, the support levels were more vague, but were not to exceed 90 percent of parity.

The 1948 Act reflected the thinking of those who wanted a return to a freer economy and less dependence on government.

The Agricultural Act of 1949, primarily a product of the southern Democrat bloc, retained in principle the flexible price-support feature of the Act of 1948, but provided for much higher levels of support.

The controversies over agricultural policy in 1948 and 1949 were largely political. The government's emergency measures did not offer long-range solutions to the farmers' problems. All that appeared to be accomplished was an increase in crop surpluses and government subsidies to farmers. What was needed was an agricultural plan that looked to the future.

Foreign demands for American agricultural products had begun to taper off, but farmers continued to produce at a high rate. While they were uneasy about their future, they were far from being in the desperate situation they had lived through in the 1930s.

The 1950 farmer was living a better life. Science was making his job easier. He was enjoying most of the comforts of his city cousin.

Things could have been better, but the American farmer was thankful for what he had.

Farmers became conscious of the bees' importance in pollinating crops. Bee farming took on an added significance as it became more than strictly honey production.

When the mink coat became the status symbol of the 40s, mink farming increased because large numbers of pelts were needed for the rebirth of the fur trade.

The "Sage of Salem" — and other curbstone lawyers and field philosophers like him — were the envy of the Washington politician. They could solve the age-old problem of the world in several minutes. Atomic bomb tests were causing it to rain too much or not enough. The government spoiled farming and the city folks were getting rich at the expense of the farmers. Despite these commentaries, progress could not be held back. The farmer was living a better life.

# XI
# New Times

## 1950-1975

Never was agricultural change and progress so dramatic as in the period 1950 to 1975. Over those 25 years, the total farm output increased more than 52 percent . . . on six percent fewer acres . . . with 60 percent fewer hours of labor. Farm production per hour of farm labor increased 279 percent.

But as is often the case efficiency grew out of adversity. In the early 1950s farmers were in a state of surplus production. This caused dramatic price drops. For example, beef prices dropped at one point from over $50 to about $20 per hundredweight and hogs dipped from above 20¢ to 8¢ a pound in parts of the Midwest. The Commodity Credit Association was empowered in 1950 to make loans on farm products in storage to support farm prices and the Department of Agriculture looked to market expansion to relieve the situation. Various attempts such as Public

Farmers are paying greater attention to the financial aspects of their operations. Computerized record-keeping services permit efficient and accurate accounting of farm finances.

President Dwight D. Eisenhower officially opened the National 4-H Center on June 16, 1959. The National Center is one of two private foundations that supports 4-H work.

Law 480 which authorized food for peace extended the use of farm products to needy countries. The Soil Bank Act of 1956 was also passed to pay farmers for taking some of their land out of production. This expensive program was not totally effective in reducing surpluses, but did help in soil conservation efforts.

In the early 1960s, the Feed Grain Program was instituted. The program paid farmers for diverting feed grain acreage to other uses and along with the Food Stamp Program helped reduce farm surpluses.

But by the early 1970s, surpluses disappeared. Worldwide weather disasters and increased foreign and commercial demand for American products swelled exports. A complete turnaround was taking place as farmers again produced more to meet demands. Yet, the nation was still operating under surplus policies which were limiting farmers' incomes. Farmers and agribusiness leaders were calling for action.

Finally, Congress passed the Agriculture and Consumer Protection Act of 1973. This legislation established target prices on commodities, limited payments to farm producers, created forestry incentives and initiated a long-range conservation program.

Farmers were free to produce at maximum efficiency. Nineteen seventy-four was a record-breaking export year, during which over $21.3 billion worth of goods were exported. This

It took 15 minutes to fill this 215-foot feed bunk with silage for 200 cows. The only human labor required for the task was flipping a switch to turn the silo unloader on and off.

Manure is being stored in its liquid state for up to six months, and spread on the fields at the farmer's convenience.

Farmers are constantly updating their knowledge of sound management practices.

represented the output of 96 million acres of U.S. cropland, or almost one-third of the acres harvested. Wheat, feed grains, soybeans, cotton, protein meal and tobacco led the way.

By 1975, agriculture was not a government burden, but the most productive force in the U.S. economy. Increased agricultural output was now viewed as an asset to help balance trade deficits. The U.S. was exporting what it produced best — food — and importing those products which other countries could produce more efficiently.

Much of agriculture's productive efficiency was brought about by the great technological changes that took place between 1950 and 1975. Many of these innovations had their roots in earlier years, but it was at this point that they were perfected and their benefits fully realized. The agricultural revolution had gained tremendous momentum.

Between 1950 and 1975, corn yields almost doubled — from 50 to over 90 bushels per acre. Cotton yields nearly doubled from 269 pounds to 520 pounds per acre. Wheat yields rose from 16.5

Harvesting tobacco has been made much more efficient by the invention of mechanical harvesters. Engineers with the USDA and Kentucky Agricultural Experiment Station developed a machine in 1963 which cut the plants off at ground level after the lower leaves were harvested by hand. Machines on the market in 1975 strip all the leaves from the tobacco stalks as they move through the field, and deposit the tobacco in wagons which ride behind.

Beginning in the early 60s concern for quality rural housing manifested itself in legislative attempts to improve the original farm housing loan program that had been started in 1949. The Farmers Home Administration (FmHA) was given authority to make housing loans in rural areas, including open country and towns with populations up to 10,000.

*Facing page:* Summertime on the farm means more than just the smell of freshly cut hay. Stacking bales as they come off the baler is a backbreaking job.

Rice came to the U.S. in 1694 when a ship from the island of Madagascar bound for England was blown off course by a storm. It was forced to land at the colony of Charleston, South Carolina. Before leaving, the captain gave the colonists a handful of rough rice grains which they used for seed. The people of the colony grew enough rice to supply South Carolina and neighboring colonies. The quality of the rice was high and an export trade with England developed. Rice production soon moved to other states and became an important U.S. crop. American rice farmers today use less than two man-days of labor per acre for all the growing and harvesting operations. In many other countries more than 400 man-hours of labor per acre are required.

By controlling a plant's exposure to daylight, it's possible to determine the plant size and time of bloom. Programmed artificial lighting makes chrysanthemums available year-round to people everywhere who enjoy them.

Fertilizer shortages have forced
American farmers to apply it as
efficiently as possible.

bushels per acre to 32 bushels and soybeans from around 22 bushels to 28.

More widespread use of mechanical innovations contributed to this improved productivity and efficiency. The 22 million work animals that required the food production from 76 million acres only three decades ago were replaced by 5 million tractors. A tractor saves a farmer 85 working days when compared to the animal power of an earlier day.

Tillage, planting and cultivation equipment paved the way for more efficient crop production. One farm equipment manufacturer recently unveiled a cultivator that operates in a 52-foot-wide swath. Its two collapsible wings each have four sections which fold in for transport.

Farmstead mechanization streamlined the job of morning and evening chores. For example, feeding the cattle and cleaning the barn is often a push-button operation. Modern milking parlors allow a dairy farmer to milk 50 to 60 cows an hour in relative comfort and ease. Fully automatic layer installations enable one man to care for 40,000 birds or more with mechanized feeding and egg gathering.

The application of pesticides became more scientific, and produced better results. Prior to World War II, control of pest-related problems was largely dependent on relatively simple compounds developed in the nineteenth century. Since the early 40s, however, scientists have developed increasingly sophisticated compounds with steadily improved selectivity and effectiveness.

The National Agricultural Chemicals Association claims that by using chemical pesticides to maximize agricultural production, farmers save Americans over $20 billion a year in food costs. While it's difficult to trace improved productivity directly and exclusively to the proper use of pesticides, their use does in-

Large commercial hatcheries turn out hundreds of chicks a day which stock the nation's broiler, layer and turkey operations. The poultry industry offers a wide range of products which rank near the top of the food list in protein value.

This Holstein cow in Pennsylvania has attained the enviable annual production of 50,759 pounds of milk. A member of the same herd was the first cow to produce over 40,000 pounds of milk in 1971.

crease crop yields and lowers the cost of food to consumers.

An experiment by the Illinois Department of Agriculture compared relative yields among nine crops — soybeans, cabbage, broccoli, tomatoes, potatoes, melons, sunflowers and two types of corn. Each crop was planted in a 12-row plot, with four rows untended; four rows receiving only mechanical cultivation for weed control; and four rows treated with modern agricultural chemicals.

The sponsors of the experiment calculated yields per acre and consumer prices of the crops grown with and without pesticides. The untended rows couldn't even be harvested.

Broccoli grown without pesticides yielded only 1,000 pounds per acre, and would have sold for $14 a pound. At the same time, the broccoli with pesticides yielded 13,000 pounds per acre for a selling price of 50 cents a pound. With tomatoes, it varied from 10,000 pounds per acre and a consumer cost of 75 cents a pound without pesticides to 30,000 pounds per acre and a cost of 25 cents a pound. The Illinois Natural History Survey analyzed the crops on which pesticides had been used and found no traces of residues. The experiment manager attributed this to the fact that

Through cross-breeding, farmers have produced animals that reflect the best characteristics of two different breeds.

*Facing page:* In a mechanized layer operation, egg gathering, handling and feeding take less than three man-hours of labor per 10,000 layers a day (cage system).

they used all pesticides according to label instructions.

Genetic improvements opened up new opportunities to the livestock producer. Artificial insemination makes it possible to spread the value of a superior bull over 50,000 calves in one year, as compared to about 30 per year by natural service. Production capabilities improved. For example, in 1974, the 50,000-pound production barrier was broken by a Holstein cow in Pennsylvania. She produced 50,759 pounds of milk in 365 days!

The infusion of European genetic stock in U.S. beef breeds is breaking old traditions for raising and feeding beef. Growthy, vigorous calves reach market weight in twelve to fifteen months and are setting new records on converting feed to beef.

Researchers are also working with artificial insemination of hogs and horses, and virtually every turkey that graces the Thanksgiving Day table is the product of artificial breeding.

Protein conversion has improved. Poultry, for example, has done a good job of efficiently converting feed to meat. Broiler

Pork production on American farms moves cyclically in response to variations in feed supplies and corn-hog ratios. Historically, pork production has increased roughly in proportion to the increase in population in the U.S.

120

producers can grow a pound of meat with less than three pounds of feed. Fish farmers are leading the way, getting a pound of fish for every pound of feed.

Other developments that made news and whose total impact is still to be felt are DNA, high-lysine corn and triticale, a new plant species resulting from a wheat-rye cross.

On July 3, 1972, the first Earth Resources Technology Satellite was launched to collect data for agriculture as well as other natural resource disciplines. The imagery and other information on crops, forestry, soils, range, natural disasters, plus environmental surveys, land use, minerals, marine resources and hydrology are helping agricultural researchers to solve earth's problems — the food shortage, energy crisis, pollution, population growth, urban decay and diminishing mineral and water resources.

Computer technology speeded up agriculture's ability to put important management techniques to work. Computerized rec-

Food processors utilize more than 90 percent of the total production of soybean oil. The rest is used for industrial products, ranging from paints to plastics.

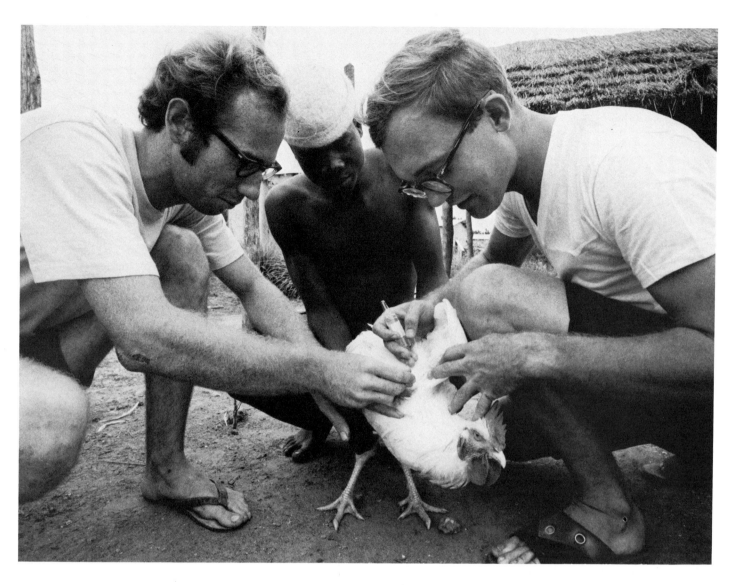

U.S. citizens with agricultural background are important members of the Peace Corps. Their work has increased agricultural productivity in underdeveloped nations.

ord keeping allowed the farmer to keep close track of his cash flow and profit and loss situation. Feed ration analysis, chemical recommendations and livestock ventilation requirements are done by computer.

Agricultural efficiency was aided by the work of Dr. Norman Borlaug, an Iowa-born scientist. Working out of CIMMYT, an international research organization originally established by the Rockefeller and Ford Foundations, Borlaug's efforts earned him the Nobel Peace Prize in 1970. In Mexico, the combination of new varieties and better management, converted the country from a wheat-importing to a wheat-exporting nation in only a few years. Virtually every country that grows wheat has been affected by this basic work. But CIMMYT's role is broader than wheat alone. The international staff of scientists is working with virtually every major world food crop. The "Green Revolution" is the label placed on their work.

These efforts by American scientists have made U.S. agricultural exports more than just farm produce. Better knowledge of the science of agriculture, better genetics and in the case of the Peace Corps, the enthusiasm, knowledge and dedication of rural youth are "exports" which advance world peace.

Another recent development in U.S. agriculture is the reliance on soybeans. From its introduction as a commercial crop scarcely 50 years ago, the soybean has gained a new level of importance and recognition. Used primarily as plow-down green manure, soybeans soon found an equally ready market as a key feed ingredient in the expanding livestock and poultry industries. Moreover, as a legume and a producer of nitrogen, the soybean provides an ideal rotation crop.

During World War II, harvested acreages of soybeans more than doubled from 4.8 million acres in 1940 to 10.4 million in 1943. But even this proved to be only the beginning. The decades of the fifties and sixties witnessed a continued production explosion unexpected by even the most farsighted of farm forecasters. The world was demanding protein, and the richest protein of all the world's oilseeds was on center stage.

During the last 25 years especially, a quality environment has been a deep concern of farmers. This stems both from philosophical beliefs and practical self-interests. Farmers and ranchers know that sustained yields of wholesome agricultural products depend upon a healthy environment. Air pollution standards have been applied to rural areas, requiring more careful attention to dust pollution, especially in the Great Plains. Environmentalists' concern about upsetting the "balance of nature" has prompted close investigation of many pesticides and the banning of some. Effluent guidelines for runoff control on large livestock operations have been implemented by the Environmental Protection Agency (EPA). The problem of disposing of animal wastes has prompted research into their

**During the last 25 years especially, a quality environment has been a deep concern of farmers.**

124

Farm crops are an important part of U.S. exports.

Norman Borlaug, the father of the "Green Revolution", developed shorter wheats and promoted complete management programs to increase yields per acre.

potential as an energy source. While farmers have been spreading manure on their fields as fertilizer for many years, only recently has manure been actively marketed as a fertilizer to the urban gardener. The full potential of animal wastes as an energy source has not yet been fully realized.

The concept of the world as "spaceship earth" is important to farmers. They know that the land, water and air resources are limited, and must be protected. Important farm management decisions always take the preservation of the environment into consideration.

The dramatic changes in agriculture have forced farmers to learn more about the hows and whys of successful farming. It's a science and school never ends. Night classes, university short courses, vocational-technical institutions and commercially sponsored workshops keep the industry abreast of rapid change.

American farmers have long been receptive to technological innovations that increase production and reduce physical labor. Since 1950 alone, the output per agricultural man-hour has increased at a rate of nearly 6 percent a year as compared to 2.5 percent for all other industries.

Thanks to the farmers' efficiency, U.S. citizens still spend a smaller percentage of their disposable income for food than any people at any time in history. In fact, food has become relatively cheaper.

If the increase in nonfarm hourly wages over the last 25 years was applied to food, a pound of round steak would cost more than $3; a quart of milk, 70¢; a dozen eggs, more than $2; and a pound of hamburger or chicken over $2.

While U.S. citizens spend 16 percent of their income on food, consumers in Asia spend 83 percent. And in the U.S. that 16 percent buys selected parts of the chicken precooked or ready to

The Williams-Steiger Occupational Safety and Health Act was passed in 1970. Initial standards included coverage for handling anhydrous ammonia, working conditions in migratory labor camps and farm vehicle safety. Recently published regulations will require the installation of ROPS (roll-over protection system) on newly manufactured tractors. Machinery guarding regulations are also being reviewed by OSHA.

Interest in increasing hay-handling efficiency prompted the manufacture of equipment to produce large round bales. Beef farmers, especially, have turned to jumbo bales for convenient feeding.

FFA members benefit from working together on various programs. By judging one another's projects, they learn more about what goes into sound farm operations.

The National Farmers Organization (NFO) initiated their own marketing program in 1975. They sold their farm products directly to consumers. At one sale in Washington, D.C., they sold 120,000 pounds of ground beef, 120,000 pounds of cheese and 90,000 pounds of potatoes.

cook in throwaway packages. In Asia, their 83 percent buys a chicken hanging by its neck in an unfrozen display. Lower relative prices in the U.S. have occurred in a period of record demand for food output.

The farmers' dependence on technology and the potential uncertainty of the market have made them susceptible to the age-old menace, the "cost-price" squeeze. Farm expenses have increased 50 percent during the last eight years, while farm income has gone up only 25 percent.

Even in the 1973-74 period when farm prices rose dramatically, the costs of fuel and fertilizer rose even faster. And increases in the price of feed grains hit the poultry producers, the dairy farmers and cattle feeders.

American farmers have proven that they are efficient. The challenge to the American public and U.S. government is to make it worthwhile for them to maintain this efficiency.

Today's grocery store is a far cry from the general store of 75 years ago. In some metropolitan areas, a configuration of bar codes signals a computer and records the price of an item on the consumer's grocery bill. As items are checked out, the computer maintains a continuous stock inventory.

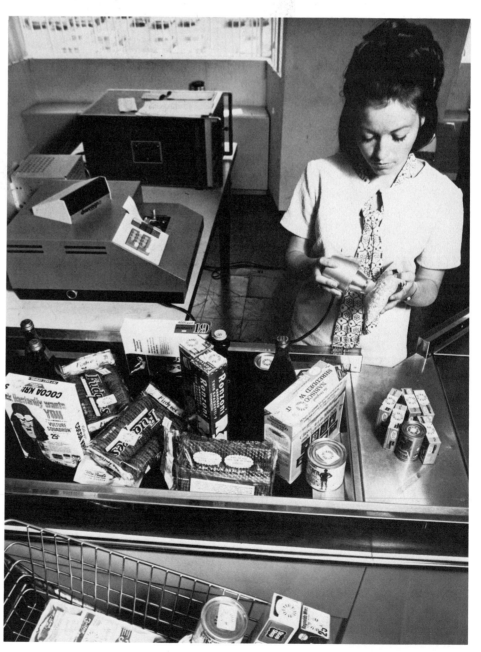

# XII
# Farming Today

Nature richly endowed American agriculture.

It produces 160 million tons of food every year or enough to fill a freight train stretching eight times the distance from New York to San Francisco. That's 2.5 tons of food for the average American family.

The land and water resources of the United States support an almost infinite variety of agricultural enterprises.

Today, 4.3 million people apply their labor and skills to produce nearly 200 crops, and manage efficient livestock and poultry operations on the 1.3 billion acres set aside for agriculture in the United States.

The average family of four consumes 2½ tons of food in a year according to USDA. That's 1,043 pounds of meat, fish and poultry, 598 pounds of fruit, 1,136 pounds of dairy products, 1,154 pounds of vegetables, 592 pounds of grain products, 229 pounds of fats and oil and 536 pounds of additional products. While quantity consumed is about the same, today's average food bill is about 17 percent of disposable income vs. 23 percent in 1951.

About three million farmers decide what crops to produce, how many acres to devote to each and how many head of livestock to raise. Paid workers represent only one-fourth of the agricultural labor force. Farming is the only major industry in the United States in which family members make up the largest share of the labor work force. Four percent of the U.S. labor force work on the farm compared with 20 percent in 1935 and 90 percent in 1776.

One U.S. farmer feeds 53 people. As a comparison, one French farmer feeds 16, one Soviet farmer feeds five, and one Indian farmer feeds four.

Farmers are more specialized. Today, the average farm has less than three major enterprises compared with over five before World War II. And this greater specialization combined with larger investments in technology have increased efficiency.

**One U.S. farmer feeds 53 people.**

The operator is also the owner on the great bulk of farms. Eighty-six percent of U.S. farms have one owner and account for 72 percent of the land in agriculture. Thirteen percent of all farms are operated under small family partnerships, with father-son partnerships accounting for 18 percent of the total land in farms.

Some large commercial operations with almost factory-type systems are located primarily in California, Arizona, southern Texas and Florida. But, less than 0.1 percent of America's farms are owned or operated by corporations with 10 or more shareholders and they account for less than 3 percent of total farm sales.

Today, there are 2.8 million farms. That's only half the number of farms for 1950. This rapid drop resulted primarily from the improved machinery and technology which permit a farm worker to handle a much larger acreage than he could 25 years ago.

In contrast to earlier times when inventions or improved practices tended to be adopted one-at-a-time, today's farmer is using a systems approach to increase agricultural productivity.

Increased reliance on technology has meant that today's farmer must buy more of the things needed for production than his ancestors did.

Farmers spend more than $60 billion a year for goods and services to produce crops and livestock. (Add to this another $15 billion for food, clothing and other consumer products and services and farmers spend $75 billion.) Farmers buy about 1 out of every 8 trucks that are sold. In a recent year they spent over $1.5 billion for tractors, $1.4 billion for automobiles and $3 billion for machinery. In time all of this will wear out, thereby creating constantly new demand for industrial output.

A farmer making his living today from farming alone must sell products worth at least $20,000 to provide his family with a minimum level of living and some return on his investment. (The average net farm income for all farms in the U.S. is $6,100 per year.)

The Northeastern States have approximately 186,000 farms that average 169 acres. This region — Maine, Vermont, New Hampshire, Massachusetts, Rhode Island, Connecticut, New York, New Jersey, Pennsylvania, Delaware and Maryland — yields 6 percent of the nation's farm output. The area produces an abundance of dairy products, broilers, vegetables and fruit.

In the Middle Atlantic States consisting of West Virginia, Virginia, North Carolina, Kentucky and Tennessee, tobacco is a top money crop. Peanuts, cattle and dairy products also rate high on the income ledger. The 481,000 farms in this region are relatively small — 127 acres on the average. But these farms account for 8 percent of the total U.S. farm production.

Peanuts are an important crop in the Southeast. This area includes South Carolina, Georgia, Alabama and Florida, and has almost 250,000 farms averaging 231 acres in size. Cotton, broilers, cattle and fruits and vegetables are also important. In Florida, citrus and winter vegetables dominate. Seven percent of the U.S. agricultural output is produced in the Southeast.

132

Cotton is still king and the favorite cash crop in the Mississippi Delta States of Arkansas, Louisiana, and Mississippi. But a lot of rice, soybeans and livestock are produced there as well. The Delta has 202,000 farms producing 6 percent of U.S. farm production. Farms again average 231 acres.

In the corn country of Iowa, Missouri, Illinois, Indiana and Ohio the fields are generally flat and nearly 60 percent of the land is in crops. The Corn Belt raises about 25 percent of all farm products in the U.S. Besides corn, the No. 1 livestock feed, many farmers raise soybeans, wheat, beef and hogs. There are 624,000 farms and they average 210 acres per unit.

133

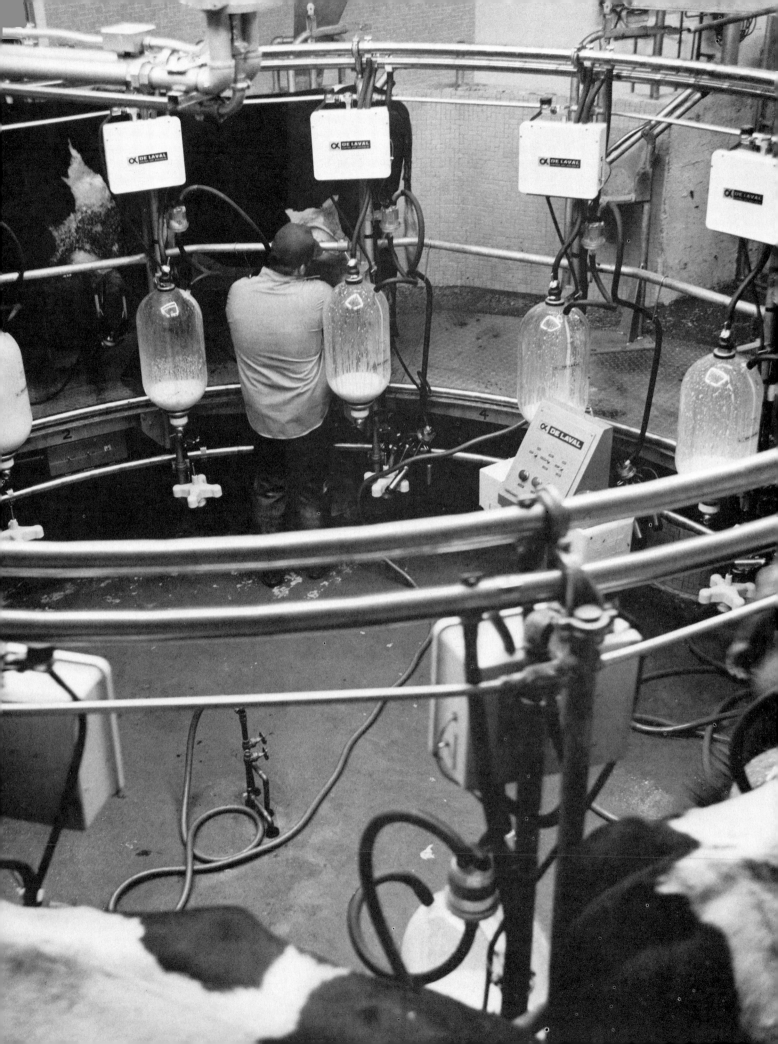

The Northern Plains (North Dakota, South Dakota, Nebraska, and Kansas) combined with the Southern Plains (Oklahoma and Texas) grow over 60 percent of the country's wheat. Rainfall is sparse, causing some farmers to put land into fallow each year to assure enough moisture to produce a crop. Large farms are the rule on the Northern Plains. There's no shortage of beef on the Southern Plains, particularly Texas, the No. 1 beef cattle state, which is also first in cotton production. The Plains states furnish nearly 25 percent of U.S. farm output.

*Facing page:* In the Midwest, the Lake States of Minnesota, Wisconsin and Michigan are suited for growing hay, forage and pasture. That's one of the reasons why this region ranks first in milk production and produces a fourth of all U.S. dairy products. Farms average about 200 acres per operation and there are about 302,000 in this area.

Long summer days make vegetable growing possible in Alaska. Major food produced on Alaska's 300 farms are dairy and poultry products.

As the level terrain yields to the rougher terrain of the Mountain States — Montana, Idaho, Wyoming, Nevada, Utah, Colorado, Arizona and New Mexico — vast expanses are ideally suited to raising cattle and sheep. Irrigation allows farmers to raise an array of crops in the valleys — sugar beets, potatoes, fruits and vegetables. The average farm has more than 2,150 acres, the most of any agricultural region. Farms total 121,000 and account for 7 percent of U.S. farm production.

Wheat and fruit are the main commodities of the Northern Pacific States of Oregon and Washington. The southern part of the Pacific region — California — produces a large family of fruits and vegetables which are grown in irrigated valleys and shipped throughout the country. Cattle are also prominent in the Pacific States. Farms number 136,000, average about 530 acres and claim 11 percent of national agricultural output.

A land of contrasts, Hawaii's 4,700 farms produce pineapples, sugarcane, and cattle. Although there are few large tracts, most farms average 25 acres. The mild climate also favors bananas, coffee, macadamia nuts and papayas.

Farmers now pay $2.7 billion annually for real estate taxes and $2.5 billion in federal and state income taxes.

About 700,000 farms (the number is growing) have gross sales of $20,000 or more and account for 80 percent of all farm product sales. Among these farms are around 70,000 (2 percent) with sales of at least $100,000 a year. These two percent produce 70 percent of our vegetables, half of our fruits and nuts and 35 percent of all poultry and poultry products.

Today's farmer may have several hundred thousand dollars invested in his farm. A typical one-man owner-operator may need $200,000 for a 360-acre Louisiana rice-soybean farm; $321,000 for a 1,950-acre Kansas wheat-sorghum farm; $769,000 for an 800-acre Indiana corn-soybean farm; and up to $611,000 for a 200-acre California vegetable farm. The largest share of the farmer's investment is in land.

**Today's farmer may have several hundred thousand dollars invested in his farm.**

In recent years over half of the farms sold have been purchased by other farmers to enlarge their operations (the average size of an American farm is 385 acres).

Farm income can fluctuate widely from year to year and even within a season, resulting from the wide swing in prices for agricultural products. One of the reasons is that crop production is not always a continuous process. Usually it covers a period of only a few months and crops can be damaged by weather, insects or disease.

Though he is a crucial part of the commercial world, the farmer continues to hold traditional rural values, according to recent surveys. Most believe that farming is essential to the well-being of the nation, that it permits independence and that it provides a favorable environment for the family.

Although many people have differing opinions as to the future of American agriculture, Theodore C. Byerly, an eminent scientist has written: "Continuing development and application of technology in production of food, fibre and forest products can supply the next generation abundantly."

Potentials for increasing crop and livestock production over the next decades are endless. Some possibilities include wider application of high-level management skills; hybrid varieties of wheat, barley and soybeans; higher protein content in grains and greater insect resistance in plant varieties. Equally important are improved breeding practices for beef cattle; multiple births in beef cattle; greater feeding efficiency and double-cropping.

What are agriculture's challenges in the years ahead? Many question the ability of the technology and resourcefulness of the U.S. production miracle to keep pace with the demands for food. At home, the American consumer is selective, discriminating, and quality-conscious. Abroad, the quantity of food needed is gigantic, with the added problem that many needy countries are not in a position to pay.

The industry must provide incentive to attract resources. The

Global attention focused on Rome in November, 1974, as delegates to the World Food Conference deliberated on the world's ability to feed its people. The conference was attended by the 130 member countries of the United Nations. Proclaiming that every human being has the "unalienable right to be free from hunger and malnutrition . . ." the conference established an early warning system on food and agriculture. U.S. farmers will play an even greater role in feeding the world in future years.

average age of the American farmer is over 50 and is the end result of the move away from farming by rural youth in the 1950s and 1960s. Keeping talented young people in agriculture is one of the keys to the future.

The threat of a continuing energy shortage focuses interest on crops as a clean and renewable energy source. They are capable of capturing energy from the sun and locking it into a useable form. Then, through fermentation, pyrolysis, reduction or combustion, the organic materials are converted to gas or liquid form for more general use. Much work needs to be done on the conversion technique.

Farmers led the American Revolution, fought its battles, supplied its food, and went on to new frontiers. Since then, the tools and technology have changed dramatically, and can be expected to change at least as much in the future. New challenges continue to be met boldly by American farmers, and on the eve of their country's bicentennial, they can feel pride in agriculture's contribution to the quality of life in the United States.

Daniel Webster said: "When tillage begins other arts follow. The farmers therefore are the founders of human civilization."

**Keeping talented young people in agriculture is one of the keys to the future.**

# Photo Credits

ACKNOWLEDGEMENTS
Sincere thanks are due to the following for supplying photographs and illustrations and granting permission to use them.

INTRODUCTION
p. 4, Library of Congress, Rare Books Division.

CHAPTER I
p. 8, Sperry New Holland; p. 9, Lexington Historical Society; p. 11, bottom, State Historical Society of Wisconsin, WHi[X3]29601; p. 12, Virginia Library.

CHAPTER II
p. 16, top, Buffalo and Erie County, New York Historical Society, B2411; p. 16, middle, State Historical Society of Wisconsin, WHi[X3]29594; p. 17, Illinois State Historical Library.

CHAPTER III
p. 24, top, State Historical Society of Wisconsin, WHi[X3]18968; p. 24, left column, State Historical Society of Wisconsin, WHi[X3]29676; p. 25, State Historical Society of Wisconsin, WHI[X3]25894; p. 26, top, State Historical Society of Wisconsin, WHi[X3]26155; p. 26, right column, Virginia State Library.

CHAPTER IV
p. 31, right column, State Historical Society of Wisconsin, WHi[X3]29135; p. 32, bottom, USDA; p. 34, Pennsylvania State University; p. 35, top, National Archives; p. 37, State Historical Society of Wisconsin, WHi[X3]29600.

CHAPTER V
p. 39, Utah State Historical Society, 385 p. 12; p. 44, left column and bottom, Land of Lincoln Barbed Wire Collectors Association; p. 46, top, USDA; p. 46, middle, The National Archives; p. 47, The Connecticut Agricultural Experiment Station; p. 49, The National Grange; p. 50, top, The National Grange.

CHAPTER VI
p. 51, Minnesota Historical Society; p. 52, bottom, Utah State Historical Society, 631.7 p.1; p. 53, middle, State Historical Society of Wisconsin, WHi(X3)29595; p. 54, top, University of Oklahoma; p. 54, bottom, State Historical Society of Wisconsin, WHi(X3)29598; p. 55, top, State Historical Society of Wisconsin, WHi(X3)29602; p. 55, middle, State Historical Society of Wisconsin, WHi(X3)29603; p. 55, bottom, State Historical Society of Wisconsin, WHi(X3)8391; p. 57, bottom, State Historical Society of Wisconsin, WHi(W6)27011; p. 58, top, J.N. Templeman, State Historical Society of Wisconsin, WHi(X18)14611; p. 58, bottom, State Historical Society of Wisconsin, WHi(X3)29599; p. 59, top, State Historical Society of Wisconsin, WHi(X3)23769; p. 60, left column, Hoard's Dairyman; p. 61, bottom, State Historical Society of Wisconsin, WHi(X3)25788; p. 62, top, Tuskegee Institute; p. 62, bottom, USDA.

CHAPTER VII
p. 64, National Archives; p. 65, National Farmers Union; p. 66, top, Albertype Collection, State Historical Society of Wisconsin; p. 67, top, USDA; p. 67, bottom, State Historical Society of Wisconsin, WHi(V2)71; p. 68, top, State Historical Society of Wisconsin, WHi(W6)11720; p. 68, bottom, USDA; p. 69, USDA; p. 70, left column, Herbert Hoover Presidential Library, 1918-20A; p. 70, top, Herbert Hoover Presidential Library, 1918-30; p. 70, bottom, State Historical Society of Wisconsin, WHi(X3)29586; p. 71, top, Herbert Hoover Presidential Library, 1916-15; p. 71, bottom, Herbert Hoover Presidential Library, 1918-2A; p. 73, top, State Historical Society of Wisconsin, WHi(D487)4521; p. 73, middle, American Farm Bureau Federation; p. 73, bottom, Future Farmers of America; p. 75, top, State Historical Society of Wisconsin, WHi(X3)29596; p. 75, bottom, Ford Motor Co.; p. 76 and 77, White Farm Equipment Co., Oak Brook, IL.

CHAPTER VIII
p. 79, top, State Historical Society of Wisconsin, WHi(X3)9090; p. 80, State Historical Society of Wisconsin, WHi(X3)24040; p. 81, top, National Archives; p. 81, bottom, State Historical Society of Wisconsin, WHi(W6)7025; p. 82, top, USDA; p. 85, right column, USDA; p. 86, Future Farmers of America.

CHAPTER IX
p. 88, top and bottom, The Kansas State Historical Society, Topeka; p. 89, top and bottom, Oklahoma Historical Society; p. 91, top and bottom, The Kansas State Historical Society, Topeka; p. 92, top and bottom, Library of Congress; p. 93, U.S. Army; p. 94 & 95, top and bottom, Tennessee Valley Authority; p. 96, USDA; p. 98, top and bottom, USDA.

CHAPTER X
p. 101, top, State Historical Society of Wisconsin, WHi(X3)29585; p. 101, bottom, State Historical Society of Wisconsin, WHi(X3)29597; p. 105, both, USDA; p. 108, State Historical Society of Wisconsin, WHi(X3)29691.

CHAPTER XI
p. 110, The National 4-H Foundation; p. 112, bottom, State Historical Society of Wisconsin, WHi(X3)29675; p. 113, top, USDA; p. 115, top, USDA; p. 119, USDA; p. 121, USDA; p. 122, top, Peace Corps, 103372-C75-27A; p. 122, bottom, Peace Corps, 31882-31-2A; p. 123, Peace Corps, 103372-C70-36; p. 125, bottom, CIMMYT; p. 126, left column, Allis-Chalmers; p. 127, top, Future Farmers of America; p. 127, bottom, National Farmers' Organization; p. 128, both USDA.

CHAPTER XII
p. 129, Du Pont Co.; p. 131, USDA-SCS; p. 132, top, USDA; p. 132, bottom, SCS; p. 133, both, USDA; p. 135, top, USDA; p. 135, bottom, USDA-SCS; p. 136, both, USDA; p. 137, USDA; p. 138, USDA-SCS; p. 140, top, Food and Agriculture Organization; p. 140, bottom, United Nations

All other photos and illustrations are from the library of Johnson Hill Press, Inc.